The

Fourth

Shock

Mobility and the Rise of
Demand Data Dominance

Ron Bienvenu

And

Matt Gauthier

The Fourth Shock

The Fourth Shock
Copyright © 2009 by Ron Bienvenu

Published by ISIS Publishing Group LLC, Connecticut

Bienvenu, Ron
The Fourth Shock: Mobility and the Rise of Demand Data Dominance.

1. Technology 2. Demand Data Analytics 3. Management 4. Supply Chain Management

ISBN 978-0-9842279-0-7 0-9842279-0-3
Printed in the United States of America.

Dedication

This book is dedicated to my beautiful wife Elvira, who always encourages me to be the bull in this china shop we call life and to my dear friend Tore James Nelson who helped me more than anyone to start this journey. Rest in peace my good man.

The Fourth Shock

Table of Contents

The Fourth Shock

Foreword

The fundamental concepts behind the supply and demand economic model affect almost every one of us on a daily basis. From the prices that we pay for our basic home utilities, to our groceries, to the stock market, all are driven by interactions between producers and consumers. Those who really understand these interactions and the rules and related strategies behind them will be the winners and the ones in the best position to maximize revenue opportunities.

And that is what this book is all about. Regardless of the size of your business, or whether you are a producer or a consumer of goods, this book will give you background and insights into the way demand information is changing the balance of power in business.

I met Ron more than two years ago when we joined forces to run a startup, and we connected immediately. If you already know Ron you know that he is one of the most brilliant folks you will ever meet, one who is great with technology *and* the business-side of the equation – I knew I was going to learn a great deal from him.

When we launched the startup our goal was to help companies improve their customer awareness and brand-recognition through a concept called "interactive advertising." This was a very Fourth Shock kind of idea where the mobile handset plays the integral role of capturing real-time consumer interactions. This demand information is then used by companies to determine the effectiveness of their advertising and marketing campaigns.

The Fourth Shock

Although the "explicit" information being captured during the interaction was very important, it was the "implicit" or hidden information that our customers often found most useful in honing their strategies and maximizing the odds of turning an interaction into a transaction. And then it hit us – what if we were to apply what we just learned to what we called "the last inches" of the supply chain? Companies around the globe spend billions of dollars annually on making the supply chain effective – from the moment an item has been produced, to where the item is while in transit, to when it reaches its destination. Yet when it comes to the fateful moment of influencing a consumer standing in the optimally sorted and arranged aisle, all of that spending is reduced to mere hope. Mobility has the potential to change that. Because almost everyone carries a mobile handset with them, it is a perfect tool for consumers to learn about the products while giving companies insights on how people actually interact with products when making a purchase decision. Any company that could effectively interact with consumers and use that information to constantly improve future interactions would gain a radical new form of competitive advantage. Therefore, demand data at the point-of-purchase became the focus of our entire business.

But getting to that realization was not an easy task. Back then we shared a lot of time together thinking, debating and arguing! You need to understand, Ron being Ron, the super smart and intellectual person that he is, makes such debates both fun and stressful and at times even painful, all at the same time! You quickly realize that you had better formulate your thoughts and words well because there is nothing he seems to enjoy more than making you eat them.

Such debates helped me personally from all angles: the technology, the business acumen and as an individual. And it was all good. He learned and I learned even more. And these concepts, which I believe helped Ron shape many of his thoughts expressed in this book, are here, available to you.

Through this book you will meet Ron and be exposed to the same provocative thought-process I had to endure for hours on end. I only hope that it helps you the reader to really understand that the Holy Grail of the supply chain actually lies in the demand side of the equation. You will find this book both informative and entertaining – if you are an executive or a store manager, an investor or shareholder, a supply chain strategist or a brand manager, or someone who is just looking to understand and master the secrets of the supply chain of the future – this book is for you.

C. Enrique Ortiz
www.CEnriqueOrtiz.com
September 2009 | Austin, Texas

Preface

This book is the culmination of years of practical experience, some profitable, some not so much, and some just too early to tell. In 1988, I moved to New York City to begin my life's adventure. While attending Louisiana State University, a roommate of mine a year ahead of me in school invited me up to sleep on the floor of his hotel room while he trained to be a stock broker at Dean Witter Reynolds. I hopped a train in New Orleans and stepped out of Penn Station in New York City. As I stumbled out onto Seventh Avenue, I couldn't have been in New York for more than 10 seconds before I knew that this was where I wanted to be. I never went home.

I took whatever work I could get. I loaded trucks at Roadway Freight in Paterson, NJ from midnight to 9:00 in the morning and then ran tickets on the floor of the commodities exchange from 10:30 am until 4:30 in the afternoon. I also worked weekends stocking shelves at A&P.

After a few months, I met a guy who knew a guy who got me an interview with a small startup company that had begun selling sophisticated research on the savings and loan industry. The minute I walked into the company I just knew they wouldn't hire me. The place was full of Ivy League types and I stood out like a sore thumb in my old wool suit that was about two sizes too small. So I marched into the owner's office and offered to make him a deal. I would work for free for two weeks and if he liked my productivity he could keep me on and pay me whatever he thought I was worth. If he didn't, I would chalk it up to experience and move on.

I would like to say this was an example of my far reaching vision, but it was more an act of desperation. Regardless, he gave me my shot and I made it work. I became a proud telemarketer at SNL Securities selling research about savings & loans companies at the height of the junk-bond fuelled crisis that gripped that industry in the late '80s. During the day I sold stuff I knew almost nothing about, and at night I would stay in the office working on technology ideas on the company's computers. Most nights I would sleep behind the filing cabinets and shower at the local gym, that is until the boss found out and forbade the practice.

Less than a year later I left SNL to start my first software company – the Vestlash Group, Inc. This was a bootstrap business in the classic sense of the word as my partner Tore Nelson and I slept on the floor of a condemned building above a liquor store in a dodgy Washington D.C. neighborhood for three years.

As a young entrepreneur I was fascinated by the greed and fear possessing grown men and women in the banking industry. As The Vestlash Group grew and evolved I learned the ins and outs of building a business from the ground up. Those were exciting times as the PC was sweeping the corporate world and I became a barely competent, self-taught computer programmer. The combination of the S&L crisis and the power of computing have both stuck with me over the years.

After selling The Vestlash Group in 1991 I started my next software company, SageMaker, in 1992. For the next nine years, through up and downs I was able to build an international business that boasted some of the largest companies in the world as customers. It was at SageMaker that I raised my first ever outside financing and completed my first acquisitions. SageMaker also happened to find itself right in the middle of the Internet euphoria of the mid-90s.

So by the time I was 33 years old I had witnessed three periods of global corporate chaos – the PC revolution of the '80s and early '90s, the S&L crisis of the 1980s, and the beginning of the Internet bubble. In those times and ever since, I have tried to keep my eyes wide open and learn equally from my successes and my failures. During that entire time I have studied how large and small corporations adapt to radical shifts in the technologies affecting their ability to compete.

After selling SageMaker in April of 2001, I have had an almost surreal life that has seen me participate in dozens and dozens of software company acquisitions of all shapes and sizes, including acting as the lead investor on a very profitable deal that turned into a full blown hostile takeover.

Through all of this M&A activity and by virtue of my service as a senior executive and board member at numerous companies, I have remained firmly plugged into the software industry.

This book is the culmination of all those experiences and the lessons learned from my interactions with the hundreds and hundreds of wonderful people I have met along the way, and the handful of jackasses who taught me a thing or two as well. As a line from and old Jimmy Buffet song goes:

> "Read dozens of books
> about heroes and crooks
> and I learned much from both of their styles."

However, one of the most important factors in writing this book came when an old friend of mine named John Sullivan contacted me about helping him build a company in the mobility software space. More than anyone else he helped me get a "deep dive" into the industry and really opened my eyes as to how close mobility was to impacting the world on an Internet-sized level.

Through John and his company I also met one of the brightest technological minds in the mobility world, C. Enrique Ortiz. Enrique's knowledge of mobility is second to none and he and John were really instrumental in the development of some of the important ideas in this book.

Finally, I would like to thank two more individuals for their insights and assistance in this endeavor, although they both may not have even realized they were teaching me so much valuable information. First is a former colleague named John Boccuzzi. John's insights and enthusiasm on the impact of demand data on large corporations served as inspiration for some of the more powerful ideas in this book. The second is my current colleague, Glenn Geho. Glenn's knowledge and understanding of demand data and the technology to handle it is encyclopedic. Furthermore, his bright and curious mind pointed me to some of the most interesting reading I have done in years on a broad array of topics, many of which influenced the ideas of the Fourth Shock.

The Fourth Shock

Introduction

In 1996, at the dawn of what would become the Internet bubble, I was the 31 year old founder and CEO of a fast growing software company. Over the next five years I had front row seats to some of the most outrageous and interesting elements of that period of "irrational exuberance". I saw billionaires and millionaires minted in seconds in stratospheric IPOs. It was a wild ride for the entire global economy. And like many wild rides, it came to an abrupt and expensive end for many participants.

The best description I can think of was that it was like riding a bull (pun intended), and all you have to do is hold on for eight seconds – an admittedly exciting eight seconds. However, even if you make it to the end of the ride, you still have to get off of the bull, and there's really no good way of doing that. All you can hope for is to be thrown clear of the thundering hooves and menacing horns, but not so far that you break your neck landing in the stands. I luckily sold my company in April of 2001, just months before the Internet bubble popped once and for all.

This wasn't the first time I had seen a euphoric market come crashing down to reality. I started my first company in 1988 near the end of the savings and loan crash that was brought about by the bursting of the junk bond bubble. I spent a year back then gathering every government filing on the S&L industry and summarizing the information for a daily electronic newsletter called the *Thrift Watch*. I had also lived through the earliest days of the PC's introduction, teaching myself BASIC on a Tandy TRS-80. And of course, like the rest of us, I recently lived through the real estate debacle of the last few years.

Through these experiences and many others, I have come to believe that irrational greed and fear are the main drivers of entirely too many major business decisions. Once these drivers set in, all too often massive amounts of resources, time and money are wasted because the participants are reacting emotionally to changing circumstances and the decisions they have previously made, or failed to make.

The Internet was a big event, and the greed and fear associated with it drove some truly strange behavior from normally balanced individuals. The Fourth Shock argues that the world once again faces a period of massive and fundamental change in the way businesses compete and profit. Like the Internet, this change is technologically driven and by its nature it can touch every single business on the planet, regardless of size or industry.

My purpose in writing this book is to help business leaders, investors and others understand how mobility will affect the world as profoundly as the Internet did in the 1990s. Specifically, readers need to understand that the last

The Fourth Shock

60 years of global supply chain development will now shift to the development of real-time demand chain information systems that will transform the global economy in unprecedented ways. This shift will mean significant threats and opportunities that will once again shuffle the global corporate pecking order.

PART I

The History of Technology Shocks

Chapter I: Shock Treatment

It's not what you don't know that hurts you; it's what you do know that ain't so.

– Will Rogers

If you are reading this, chances are you are an educated, well-rounded individual who understands that certain inventions have had a profound impact on the development of human society. Therefore, the following question should be a simple one for you to answer:

Who invented the internal combustion engine?

Surely you would agree that this invention literally changed the entire world in a relatively short period of time. Modern warfare, mega-cities, energy production and consumption, the global warming debate and suburban living are almost unthinkable without it. It brought about massive industrialization, the petroleum industry and blitzkriegs. The current geo-political reality in which we live, where oil and access to it are rightly considered strategic issues by the most powerful nations on earth, would most certainly be very different today if not for this invention.[1] Yet, I have asked this simple question literally hundreds of times to thousands of people and only twice has anyone ever even come close to answering it.

It vexed me to no end to understand why the majority of well-educated, business savvy people, cannot answer this simple question. After pondering this interesting puzzle for the last few years, I came to the following conclusion: no one knows because it is almost impossible to pinpoint one specific invention or inventor,[2] but more importantly, it is ultimately irrelevant to the world at large. Let me explain.

Assume this is the year 1900. It's the dawn of the 20th century and one of the most exciting and optimistic periods in human history and you are the proud owner of a very successful textile mill. Also assume that I am a young, energetic and capable salesman for the Paradigm Shift Motor Company located in Engine City, Michigan. I call on

---

[1] See Daniel Yergin's *The Prize* for a fascinating read on the history of oil and its impact on the global economy.

[2] To answer the question, German inventor Nicolaus Otto was the first to invent a working internal combustion engine to efficiently burn fuel in a piston chamber. Using the Otto Cycle, Dr. Rudolf Diesel – another German inventor who was actually born in France – created the Diesel engine, which despite many other models appearing after Otto's and before his, became the first commercially successful internal combustion engine.

your firm one fine sunny day and inform you that I have in my possession a truly amazing machine, one that is sure to transform the world as we know it. A machine so efficient it is literally hundreds, no one thousand times more efficient than the best steam driven engines in your production facilities. I go on in a tone that only a true believer can muster and swear to you that if you would be so kind as to give me 30 minutes of your valuable time, I will show the future of manufacturing – check that, the future of mankind.

You look at me slightly amused and note that you've heard something about this newfangled machine. Continuing on, you admit you are slightly curious, but you also make it clear that you doubt very seriously you would be willing to buy today. Undaunted, I saunter into your office with my tiny engine (as compared to the steam behemoths to which you are accustomed) and proceed to start 'er up. Despite being a bit noisy, the machine really does appear to live up to its billing. As the camshaft spins round and round at incredible speeds, you become mesmerized as thoughts of cost savings dance through your head. I remind you of course, good salesman that I am, that not only will you be able to experience huge savings on fuel cost, but just think of all the real estate you will save by relegating those monstrous steam engines to the trash heap. And not only that, but you will also be able to get rid of layers of soon-to-be unionized employees as this new engine is easier to maintain and far more productive.

As I continue to earnestly pepper you with all the wonderful things this new engine brings to your business, you sense yourself getting caught up in the moment. You feel the thrill of seeing something you are sure will change the world and you can hardly contain your delight that you will get to be a part of it all. Your mind races with the new problem of dealing with the excess real estate in all those factories of yours and you can't wait to get to a dinner party and tell all your friends about your brush, and likely involvement with the future.

Like a lioness in the brush closing in on its prey, I sense the time for closing this sale is at hand, so I ask how many of these truly amazing, dare I say, revolutionary machines would you like to order today. Slightly agitated that I interrupted the delightful dinner party being played out in your head, you are drawn back into reality and begin to come to your senses. The whir of the machine is hypnotic, but you didn't build a successful textile company by getting all emotional about silly machines. And then you give me your answer...none.

None? None?! How can this be? Surely you see the benefits of my product? You undoubtedly know that you have been graced by the presence of the future in your own office today? Once the shock of your answer starts to wear off, I almost become angry. How can you not believe? What are you some kind of Luddite?[3] Don't you understand

---

[3] Wikipedia entry: The Luddites were a social movement of British textile artisans in the early nineteenth century who protested—often by destroying mechanized looms—against the changes produced by the Industrial Revolution, which they felt

The Fourth Shock

that you will either buy my product or perish? This is binary. I decide you deserve your fate, but I have to ask what would drive someone to say no to the future. Your answer – gasoline.

Gasoline? Gasoline?! Ok. So now it is clear. You are a Luddite.

You sound apologetic as you state that of course you believe that I am onto something and that you really feel that you may have glimpsed the future today. But you point out a glaring problem with my wonderful product – just where are you going to get a steady, reliable and reasonably priced supply of gasoline to run this new fangled machine? You note with the wisdom of your years that the world's most respected geologists think that the total known supply of petroleum may only last 10 to 15 years. Now I am really shocked at your attitude. Not that the world's supply of petroleum may be short lived (I already knew that), but that you are thinking 10 to 15 years into the future!

You sink back into your chair with a bemused grin on your face, noting how consistently striking it is that those who are the most excited about the future are almost always the ones who have had the least amount of experience in the past.

You sense my barely hidden anger and attempt to explain. But, it is unnecessary as your point is not lost on me. Like an annoying pebble lodged intractably in my

---

were leaving them without work and changing their entire way of life.

21

shoe, I know deep in my soul that you have a point. You explain in sober terms that you cannot risk a going concern on the promises of an untried and unreliable new technology.

I splutter a few reminders of the coming revolution and all the benefits it will bring. I remind you of the cost savings and tremendous value you are passing up. Then, with an air of sincere arrogance, I gather my miracle machine and march out of your office. As I do so, I am almost saddened by the inevitability of your demise, but I am even more annoyed by the gnawing splinter that has been planted in my mind due to your silly outburst about the continued availability of steady and affordable gasoline supplies.

And this is the story of invention. Technological advances with the potential to touch nearly every part of society have never existed in a vacuum. Name the invention: fire, the wheel, writing, the printing press, electricity, automobiles, air travel, computers, the Internet – they all required the development of supporting infrastructure to deliver their impact on the world.

Just as each technical marvel was itself built on the foundation of ideas and information that came before it, making such an invention practical and useful requires subsequent waves of innovation. The preceding sales call typifies the early stages of any "revolutionary" technology. The innovation itself almost always has fairly obvious value and potential, but as Mike Ditka, snarling coach of the 1985 Chicago Bears is reported to have said, "Potential only means you haven't done sh*! yet." Therefore, the greater problem often lies in finding critical uses for the invention rather than the perceived potential value for it and that often requires a myriad of other brilliant ideas in order to make it commercially viable.

It is in this vein that the Fourth Shock shifts from a potentiality to a near-term inevitability because it rests on the foundation of three previous shocks to the global economy that were brought about by advances in information technology. Over the past 70 years, these three great leaps forward have increased efficiencies across the globe and helped bring about the greatest explosion of wealth and knowledge the human race has ever witnessed.

For example, if this were the year 1996 rather than 2009, the title of this book would be The Third Shock and I would be explaining how the Internet, and more specifically the commercialization of the Internet was going to change the world. You would be forgiven if you responded with more than a fair amount of skepticism at the time. In that year, I was a starry-eyed entrepreneur trying to raise money for the first time in my life from venture capitalists and many of them were doubtful as well.

My company, SageMaker, was a fairly straight forward enterprise infrastructure company, so arguably I had an easier time of persuading investors that we had a shot than the wildly innovative companies of the time. But let's assume for a moment that you were that venture capitalist and I was trying to get you to invest in another idea for a software company that was truly leveraging the power of the Internet. One pitch of the day would have gone something like this:

> Starry-Eyed Entrepreneur: "You know, this Internet thing is going to be huge."

> Grizzled, Ruthless Venture Capitalists: "Oh yeah, and how the hell are we supposed to make money from it?"

> Starry-Eyed Entrepreneur: "I'm not sure, but I am telling you it is gonna be big and affect everything."

> Grizzled, Ruthless Venture Capitalists: "You think it could affect you into getting me a latte?"

> Starry-Eyed Entrepreneur: "Be serious here! Ok, ok, here's my idea, we start a Web site where lower income people can go to sell Pez dispensers and used clothing! Brilliant right?"

Assuming you didn't simply toss me out of your office, you might take sadistic pleasure in explaining the many, many obvious problems with my so-called brilliant idea. For starters, you might point out that in 1996 few people knew what a Web site was and no one had ever demonstrated that you could make money from one. The fact that my Web site targets people who probably don't even own a computer, much less an Internet connection, would constitute another glaring example of my ignorance. And finally, who in their right mind would want to trade Pez dispensers and, God forbid, used clothing?

Of course, it would be you who would be proven to be painfully ignorant as the company now known as eBay would eventually get funded and thrive. But in fairness to my venture capitalist friends, I would have never gotten that investment either. Heck, I may have missed Amazon, Google, Yahoo!, and E*Trade as well.

Regardless of whether or not any of us would have been smart enough to invest in eBay, the fact remains that the Internet had a tremendous impact on nearly every aspect of the global economy. I was lucky enough to be right in the middle of it and to put it mildly, it was interesting. I had a front row seat to one of the most radical transformations of the global economy of all time and tellingly, I see it all happening again.

Today, 4.1 billion human beings amble around the earth carrying a two way communication device.[4] Be it a cell phone, smart phone or a Skype-enabled notebook computer, "mobility" is poised to shake the very foundations of the global economy in at least as profound a way as the Internet did in the 1990s. Hopefully, the world has learned some valuable lessons about "bubbles" and

---

[4] Source: 2009 Survey by the International Telecommunications Union (ITU)

hyperbole when it comes to financing the next big thing, because ready or not, mobility is poised to have a dramatic impact on the way the world works.

Interestingly, a good way to describe the impact of mobility on the global economy can be found in the field of evolutionary biology. In 1972, paleontologists Niles Eldridge and Stephen Jay Gould published a groundbreaking paper entitled *Punctuated Equilibria*. Although Gould humbly stated at the time that most of the ideas were Eldridge's, he has been linked in popular culture with the overall idea. Without exploring the technical arcana surrounding the nuances of the neo-Darwinist evolutionary debate, the Theory of Punctuated Equilibrium generally holds that evolution rarely occurs and that long periods of stasis are occasionally interrupted by rapid, catastrophic change. In periods of stasis, most mutations fail as the ecosystem and the species that make up the environment are in balance. This is not to say that all evolution ceases, but the types of evolution tend to be gradual and within species rather than the radical creation of totally new species. An opposable thumb here, a new color variation there, etc., but rarely does an entirely new species arise in times of stasis.[5]

---

[5] Interestingly, Clayton M. Christensen's book, *The Innovator's Dilemma* makes a very similar argument related to business competition in his discussions about the difference between "Disruptive technologies" and "Sustaining technological changes."

The Fourth Shock

However, every so often a fundamental shock to the environment occurs and all hell breaks loose as the ability to radically mutate becomes a huge advantage in an evolutionary sense of the word. In these periods of punctuation, evolution, as supported by the geologic record, tends to explode as incumbents in the old environment are replaced by new species better adapted to the now changed environment. For example, the earth has gone through at least four major "ice ages" and subsequent periods where the Earth was virtually ice free, even in high latitudes.[6] In each shift of the general environment, the criteria for survival changes. White bears in the jungle are a pretty bad idea as prey can see the predator coming and flee. The same is true for black bears in the snow.

Once a new period of equilibrium is reached, species tend to adapt to the now stabilizing environment and consolidate their gains. Radical mutations are once again punished in the new period of relative stasis. One way of looking at this process is that it is an attempt for living species to understand demand data. What does the new environment demand in order to be successful?

As stated earlier, this exploration of Gould's theory serves as a reasonable parallel for the business world as well. The Fourth Shock argues that the global economy has endured three significant information technology shocks

---

[6] As far as I can tell, the last ice age, which peaked approximately 20,000 years ago, was not caused by human activity.

over the past 70 years that have each transformed the world – with winners and losers rising and falling in each period. It also predicts that a fourth technology shock is rapidly approaching that is so fundamental it will impact nearly every business and consumer on the planet. Furthermore, this new technological shift differs significantly from the first three shocks in one very radical way that will make its impact even more difficult to predict.

Namely, the Fourth Shock will usher in a new era of information technology focused on capturing, analyzing and acting on demand data in real-time. Prior information technologies that have been implemented by business have been almost exclusively focused on the supply side of the supply/demand relationship. This was originally driven by "just-in-time manufacturing" and intensive inventory management and later by pushing computing power and information to the edges of the organization and beyond. But it was always reactive, driven by the idea that can be summed up by the following: sell something, do something.

The Fourth Shock will be fundamentally different because it ushers in a world where real-time demand takes center stage. Therefore, in 20 years we may look back and, with the wisdom of hindsight, argue that the Fourth Shock was really the First Shock of a whole new era of information technology that shifted the focus from a supply-centric view of the world to a demand-centric one.

Either way you look at it, demand data is poised to supplant supply chain centric views of corporate organization and operations. Furthermore, one-to-one, real-time consumer interactions will wreak havoc on traditional mass media advertising and marketing. Companies that get this right will generate greatly increased profits from the same set of assets and gain market share in a virtuous cycle of value. Perhaps even more importantly, corporations will be able to construct unique and sustainable barriers to entry through the accumulation and management of demand data.

Sustainable barriers to entry from unique demand data? One-to-one consumer interactions? Earning more profit without significantly higher investments in assets? While all of this may border on the strange and fantastic, I intend to prove to you my dear reader that not only is all of this inevitable, it is already here and about to explode into the mainstream consciousness of the business world.

Years ago, I recall reading an interesting way of looking at significant world changes that was written by none other than that most successful of Communists, Mao Tse Tung. Granted, it may be a bit odd to reference one of the most virulent enemies of capitalism in a book about how capitalism and capitalists will once again change the world in a fundamental way. However, I think we can often find pearls of deep wisdom in our most passionate enemies.

Mao was one of the most successful generals of the 20th century, a period of time that had no shortage of generals, nor the unfortunate need for them. As a founding member of the Chinese Communist Party, he fought a long war against the Japanese and led the victorious side in a violent civil war against the Chinese Nationalists. In what is now known in China as The Long March, Mao led the beleaguered Communist army out of an encircled position and proceeded to march his forces thousands of miles over some of the most inhospitable lands in China. This allowed the Communists to regroup and eventually become victorious in the civil war but at a cost of nearly 90% of his forces. In an interview with the American correspondent, Edgar Snow in 1936 following this arduous ordeal, Mao calmly stated that he was certain that the Communists would prevail over their enemies because only the strongest soldiers were left in his army. If that doesn't sound like every entrepreneur I have ever met, I don't know what does.

In one attempt to explain what he saw as inevitable victory over occupying Japanese forces, he used the example of a scale with two sides. On the right side sits 50 lbs. and on the left there is nothing. If we add 1 lb. to the left side, the scale does not move. We can do this 48 more times until there are 49 lbs. sitting on the left side and still nothing. When we add just one more pound, the scale moves towards balance. It is at this point that all the pundits and visionaries will point and say, "Aha, that last pound caused a change in the balance of the situation." Furthermore, if we were to add just one more pound, the entire situation will be completely reversed as the left side will glide towards the ground. Again the pundits will point and gawk and overstate the impact of the last two pounds relative to the overall situation. Mao argued that the ability to see the 48 lbs. sitting there on the scale is far more important than merely pointing out the obvious after the fact.

The Fourth Shock

In essence, the Fourth Shock argues that there are 48 lbs. sitting on the left side of the scale when it comes to the impact of new technologies allowing companies to capture and leverage new types of demand data that are available for the first time in human history. Driving this insight are two specific factors that are relatively new to the world:

1) the availability of point-of-sale data from a wide range of ever growing sources in time frames that are rapidly approaching real-time, and

2) the fact that 4.1 billion active mobile subscriptions are in use creates the unprecedented opportunity to interact with a majority of the world's consumers at the point when they are about to make a buying decision regardless of where they are on the globe.

Corporations and the investors who fund them can no longer afford to ignore the fact that new technologies are once again poised to change the competitive landscape for every business regardless of size or location. They must develop the capability to digest ever increasing amounts of demand data in shorter and shorter time frames, analyze and interact with that data, choose a course of action, and then get that information back to a consumer standing in an aisle, all within seconds. This is not science fiction. It already happens every day around the globe and it is rapidly becoming mainstream. When it does, it will permanently alter the balance of power in nearly every industry.

The Fourth Shock

The Fourth Shock is the moment in time when the commercialization of mobility reaches critical mass and impacts the way every business operates. Mobile technology and the ability to interact with consumers in real-time at the point-of-purchase, combined with the unprecedented availability of point-of-sales data in near real-time, are the technological drivers of the Fourth Shock. But just like the Internet before it, technology is only part of the picture.

The more important aspect of the Fourth Shock is the way it will shift the competitive landscape in nearly every industry. Companies that most effectively figure out how to take advantage of these technological changes will begin to build historical databases of unique data that will serve as the foundation for sustainable competitive advantage. By the time their competitors start to act, the laggards will find themselves at a permanent disadvantage from a demand data perspective. The companies with an advantage in demand data will possess an informational advantage that can inexorably force their competitors down a path of ever shrinking market share and eventual extinction.

Chapter II: The First Shock: Digitization

In the beginning was the Word;
and the Word was with God
and the Word was God.
(John 1:1-4)

Information, wealth and power have always had a close relationship. Modern ideas of data can trace their origins all the way back to the end of the 4th millennium BC and the dawn of the written word. Around that time, writing evolved out of economic necessity as the Sumerians marked clay tokens as a means of keeping account of commodities. These tokens eventually became clay tablets on which numbers were recorded by means of pressing a sort of stylus into them. As time went on, the common stylus improved and became sharper, offering more detail in the writing.

The Fourth Shock

During the first few hundred years of the 3rd millennium BC, Sumerian writing began to resemble something like phonetics, and by the 26th century BC the Sumerian's written language had advanced to the point where it was almost as fluid and robust as their spoken one. It didn't take long for Sumer's trading partners from other cultures to see the benefits of the written word. Soon the idea spread rapidly in various localized forms throughout the ancient world, initially in and around the Fertile Crescent in present day Iraq.

Even in those times, it seems that keeping track of supply and demand was the fundamental purpose of writing and numbers. As a matter of fact, the earliest calculating devices predate the Sumerian culture by millennia. One such device is a *tally stick* made from the fibula of a baboon dating back approximately 20,000 years. The *Ishango Bone*, as it is known, was discovered in 1960 and has a series of tally marks carved in three columns running the length of the tool. Some scientists have even gone so far as to suggest that the notches indicate a mathematical understanding that goes beyond counting.

The advent of writing took heretofore primitive efforts to the next level and unleashed a series of increasingly ingenious devices to capture, store and calculate information. But it wasn't really until the 19th century that computing devices began to move in the direction that would lead to the First Shock - digitization of information.

In 1801, a Frenchman named Joseph Marie Jacquard invented a loom that weaved patterns automatically by following a series of holes punched into paper cards. The cards were interchangeable, and although threading the loom was substantially more labor-intensive than traditional means, it marked the first time that coded information was used to control the operation of a machine. Jacquard's machine was not terribly successful as a commercial apparatus, but at this time the industrial revolution was in full swing and this seemingly insignificant invention unleashed the imaginations of an entire generation of inventors.

Once such inventor was Charles Babbage, who in 1837 put forth a design for what he called his "Analytical Machine" that would be able to perform arithmetic operations and square roots. Furthermore, his planned machine would store values and, borrowing a page from the Jacquard loom, the programs and data would be input into the machine in the form of punched cards. Unfortunately, Babbage died in 1871 before he could finish building his machine, but later inventors demonstrated that his ideas were sound and for that Babbage is often cited as the father of modern computing. Readers who worked with computers in the 1950s, '60s and '70s will recall the punch cards of the day, and they have Mr. Babbage to thank or curse for it.

At the end of the 19th century, Herman Hollerith, a German-American from Buffalo, New York, invented the mechanical tabulator that could actually read information off of punch cards in the form of data. The idea was that holes punched in specific places corresponding to numbers on punch cards could represent a great deal of data. Soon after he filed for a patent on his idea, Hollerith began working for the United States Census Office where he built tabulating machines to more efficiently process the large amount of census data collected every ten years. And boy was it effective. It took over eight years to process the 1880 census data, but using Hollerith's machines, the 1890 census took only one year. In 1911, Hollerith's company merged with three others to form the Computer Tabulating Recording Corporation, which several years later changed its name to the now famous International Business Machines Corporation.

The next big step forward for computing came in 1936 when a young British genius by the name of Alan Turing published a groundbreaking paper that described a method for using algorithms in computing machines. An algorithm is simply an effective method for solving a problem using a finite sequence of instructions. The Turing Machine, as it became known introduced the concept of the programmability of machines by performing one step at a time on a paper tape that was fed through the machine. It was an abstract idea that was subsequently expanded upon, but it has been proven that with just this simple procedure the machine can be made to simulate the logic of any basic computer algorithm. The importance of this invention far exceeds the scope of this book, but suffice it to say that in 1999 *Time* Magazine named Turing to its list of the 100 Most Important People of the 20th Century.

The Fourth Shock

All of these inventions were a progression towards an event that was fast becoming an unknown necessity – the digitization of information, a.k.a. the First Shock. It is simply one of the most important things to happen to the world in recent history, arguably rivaling the discovery of DNA, the theory of evolution, or the theory of relativity.[7]

Granted, "digitization of information" flows off the tongue like sticky peanut butter and on its surface doesn't seem all that amazing. What can be so damned important about 0's and 1's anyhow? A good place to start is with the father of information theory, Claude Shannon.

While in graduate study at MIT in 1937, Shannon wrote a master's thesis describing how Boolean logic – the mathematics of dealing with 0's and 1's – could be used to design better relays in telephone routing switches. That paper has since come to be one of the most famous theses ever written. At the time however, all it earned Shannon was a little notoriety by being published, praise from his peers, and most significantly a job working in the research arm of AT&T, the famous Bell Laboratories. At Bell Labs, Shannon went to work on trying to figure out just how much capacity a telephone line could carry or more specifically, how many conversations could go on

---

[7] In his book *Decoding the Universe*, Charles Seife argues that in addition to the many information based marvels of our times, information theory may one day solve some of the world's greatest mysteries such as the heretofore unexplainable conflicts between Relativistic and Quantum Physics.

simultaneously on a single line without interference. Since the transmission of voice on a telephone wire is really the transmission of voice information, the question was really about how much information could fit on such a wire.

As he began to work on this project, Shannon thought about the nature of information – something that helps you to answer a question. With his background studying Boolean logic – again the mathematics that manipulates 0's and 1's – he hit upon the idea of applying those 0's and 1's as answers to questions. At the concept's most basic level, let's say that 1 means yes and 0 means no. Are you reading this book right now? 1. Is it the year 1886 as you do so? 0. This is a simple way of encoding the informational answers to "yes" or "no" questions. Shannon's great insight came when he realized that this kind of encoding could be used to answer *any* question that had a finite answer.

For example, these lowly 0's and 1's, which Shannon and his colleagues termed "bits," could be applied to the letters of the alphabet, with a different code of bits given to each letter. Extending this idea further, any word or group of words that had an actual ending could be encoded into 0's and 1's as well. Shannon had stumbled onto a method for creating the universal medium of information much in the same way that the four amino acids of DNA are the universal building blocks of life on our planet. Seemingly innocuous strings of 0's and 1's became the foundation for a veritable Rosetta Stone for any and all information in the world.

The Fourth Shock

One very important benefit of converting information into binary bits is its potential for compression. This, as Charles Seife points out in his book *Decoding the Universe*, is due to redundancy in language. We can find a basic example of this in most vowel usage. You've probably seen one of those lines before that shows the mind's ability to process words even with letters missing. W-ll th-s -s pr-tty m-ch r-ght. Similar to the human mind's ability to read a sentence missing some of its letters, a computer can do the same with unnecessary letters, input errors, and other erroneous aspects of files. Thus a text file can be massively compressed on a computer's hard drive. As Seife points out, "One of the great victories of Shannon's information theory is in formally defining redundancy and figuring out precisely how much information can be carried in a stream of symbols – redundant or otherwise."[8]

Shannon's theory served as the bedrock of information theory, and it was a short trip from there to the construction of new kinds of machines that could take advantage of it. The first electronic digital computer of real note was called the ENIAC, which stood for Electronic Numerical Integrator and Computer. It could add and subtract 5000 times faster than any other machine in the world at the time. It could also multiply, divide and calculate square roots. Built at the University of Pennsylvania in 1945, ENIAC was the most sophisticated computing machine ever built. For all its computing advantages over other machines in the

---

[8] Charles Seife, *Decoding the Universe* p. 71

world, ENIAC definitely paid in bulk. The machine measured 8.5 feet x 3 feet x 80 feet, and it weighed in at a svelte 30 tons. It boasted five million hand-soldered joints. Quite different from the laptops we enjoy today, but it *was* the first general purpose electronic digital computer.

ENIAC spawned what was to become the golden era of mainframe computing. The earliest of the commercially used mainframe computer models included the UNIVAC 1, the IBM 701, the LEO 1 and their contemporaries. All of these computers shared the common trait of being gargantuan in size and they were all made in the earlier half of the 1950s. UNIVAC 1, in fact, was the first "mass produced" computer, eventually selling a whopping 46 machines. Shannon's idea was getting its mileage.

All of the computers produced during this time were commonly referred to as the "First Generation," and they were produced in relatively large numbers from the early '50s into the '70s. In the late '60s, competition to build and improve these earliest models was extremely intense and primarily divided amongst eight companies: IBM, UNIVAC, Burroughs, Honeywell, General Electric, NCR, Control Data and RCA. IBM held a substantial lead throughout this period, prompting industry analysts to label the industry as "IBM and the Seven Dwarfs."

Improvements accelerated quickly in the 10 years following ENIAC's development, and by 1954 IBM introduced the IBM 650 which was positively anorexic at 2000 pounds. In addition to its much more manageable size, IBM aggressively priced its new mainframe and introduced the concept of leasing into the computer world. These developments laid the groundwork for the eventual development of minicomputers, which in turn would bridge the gap between these giants and the modern PCs of the Second Shock.

Another huge step towards the arrival of the modern PC came in the 1950s with the general availability and integration of transistors into computers. As these began to replace the unwieldy vacuum tubes common in First Generation computers, Second Generation computers became simultaneously more affordable and more powerful. "Smaller, swifter and smarter" would be the constant theme of computing all the way to the present time.

The First Shock was as fundamental to human society's development as Gutenberg's printing press was in his day. As soon as Shannon proved in his thesis that information could in fact be digitized, the race for making the next machine to best do so was on and continues just as vibrantly and vigorously as it did 60 years ago. More importantly, the First Shock is the foundation upon which sits the modern global economy and its ability to instantly move information around the world at the speed of light. It was the first significant change in the way humans create, record, distribute and use information since the age of the Sumerian culture. Think about it. Before the advent of information theory and the mainframes that were built to take advantage of it, large corporations were using pen and paper to record inventories, sales, and finances in pretty much the same way the Sumerians used clay tablets carved with sharp objects.

These enormous leaps in computer processing power led directly to the creation of modern supply chain solutions. Once mainframe computers became available to businesses, the first thing they did was to start recording inventory and sales levels. Sell something, do something. The 1960s and '70s witnessed the emergence of a significant increase in global competition and major corporations were desperate to expand internationally and find ways to be more competitive. Early computers helped in both efforts.

Digitized information allowed for greater inventory management capabilities and for financial controls to be centralized, thereby giving management teams the information they needed to more effectively execute global expansion. This was incredibly important, but nothing did more to expand the creation of the modern supply chain than the drive for greater competitiveness, and in particular the concept of "just-in-time" manufacturing.

According to the Wikipedia article: "Just-in-time (JIT) is an inventory strategy that strives to improve a business's return on investment by reducing in-process inventory and associated carrying costs…JIT can dramatically improve a manufacturing organization's return on investment, quality, and efficiency."

The technique was hardly new, as Henry Ford described it in his 1922 book, *My Life and Work*: "We have found in buying materials that it is not worthwhile to buy for other than immediate needs. We buy only enough to fit into the plan of production, taking into consideration the state of transportation at the time. If transportation were perfect and an even flow of materials could be assured, it would not be necessary to carry any stock whatsoever. The carloads of raw materials would arrive on schedule and in the planned order and amounts, and go from the railway cars into production. That would save a great deal of money, for it would give a very rapid turnover and thus decrease the amount of money tied up in materials. With bad transportation one has to carry larger stocks."[9]

But what was new was the ability to move information about resources in real-time around the globe. This allowed for greater coordination of production facilities regardless of their location, and this in turn led to the increased ability of large companies to efficiently and profitably enter new geographic markets.

Both of these ideas were instrumental in the whole concept of "globalization" as we know it today, and that was all made possible by the First Shock. Although mainframes created new possibilities for corporations, there were significant limitations relating to their use that hampered widespread deployment.

For starters, mainframes could store and process massive amounts of data, but they were exceptionally difficult to work with because they required a highly specific set of knowledge by the user. You just didn't walk

---

[9] Wikipedia entry: Just-in-time (business)

up to a mainframe terminal and start hacking away. You had to schedule time to enter the mainframe room with the mainframe gatekeepers, run your processes, and hope that everything went smoothly without one of the many errors of the day. If you got it wrong, you would be required to go figure it out and perhaps you could get another time slot tomorrow to try again. It quickly became obvious that having one centralized computing station was suboptimal as demand for computing time far exceeded capacity.[10] Responding to this need, the computer manufacturers began to develop smaller versions of the mainframe known as mini-computers. Despite the moniker, these machines were far from the miniature computers we see today, but they were much smaller and cheaper than mainframes and they could be cost-effectively deployed across the divisions of a large enterprise.

The ever-increasing need for businesses to keep track of products, parts, sales, etc., along with the new capability of storing that information digitally on mainframes and then on minicomputers, initially gave birth to the first software accounting packages and manufacturing inventory control systems. These systems were later combined together and with other "modules" evolved into what is now called

---

[10] Recognizing this demand problem, in 1962 Ross Perot founded EDS and signed an agreement to buy unused time on Southwestern Life Insurance's IBM 7070 mainframe computer. He then began selling this unused time, usually weekends and the wee hours of the morning, to other companies that couldn't afford a mainframe but needed computer time to process information.

"enterprise resource planning" or ERP. Today, ERP systems serve as the backbone of the modern supply chain, moving information seamlessly from the point-of-sale all the way to the manufacturing facility – sell something, do something.

Another interesting development from the First Shock springs from the fact that the distribution of computing power across an organization created the need to connect and coordinate these computers. In turn, this gave rise to the networking technologies which ultimately culminated in the Third Shock – the commercialization of the Internet.

However, before the Third Shock could have its profound impact on the business community and the world, a second layer of infrastructure would need to be implemented.

Chapter III: The Second Shock: The Personal Computer

"I don't think it's that significant."
- Tandy president John Roach on IBM's entry into the microcomputer field

On August 12, 1981, IBM introduced its "Personal Computer" and began competing head-to-head with industry leaders Tandy, Commodore International and Apple. As the quote introducing this chapter states, Tandy president John Roach wasn't too impressed. In May of 1993, Tandy sold its computer business and exited the industry. The PC's birth was one of the twin pillars of the Second Shock. The other component was the fact that the PC shipped with a brand new 16-bit computer operating system called MS-DOS from a little unknown firm called Microsoft.

The Fourth Shock

This unlikely pair, the largest and most famous technology firm in the world and a group of geeky kids, would unleash the power of computing around the globe. In the process, they created an entirely new industry – the enterprise software industry – and spread computing power to the edges of every corporation and institution in the world.

The Second Shock wasn't just the introduction of a new, more affordable type of computer. It was the fact that people in parts of companies that had never heard of a computer were about to be forced to use them and, that by establishing a critical mass of consumers of PCs and the MS-DOS operating system, a whole generation of primarily kids were about to start producing software for every conceivable market solution.

Those of you ancient enough to remember working with computers during the 1980s might remember that the biggest challenge facing the mystified employees dealing with these newfangled and endlessly frustrating machines was getting the darned things to interface correctly with the printer and print documents. I am not exaggerating when I say that the first people to become the head of information technology (IT) departments were more often than not the curious individuals who could figure out how to get the printer to work.

IBM's impetus for developing the PC was a desire to make further inroads into the small computer market that was slowly but steadily becoming a mass market. The first step on this trend began in the late 1960s with the introduction of the minicomputer. Although hardly "mini" by modern standards, compared to the mainframes of the day they were positively dainty – about the size of an average refrigerator. However, like the mainframe, the minicomputer was a multi-user computer, meaning that a company or institution would not have one for every user, but rather many users would share the use of one machine. Companies that made the minicomputer throughout the '70s and '80s were the likes of IBM, Data Equipment Corporation, Data General and Hewlett-Packard.

Despite its dominance in the "big metal" mainframe and minicomputer markets, the continued technology advancements in computer processing power was moving the market towards consistently smaller and cheaper devices and IBM was determined to be part of it. Since the platform of minicomputers was set up for multiple users, individual end users were reliant on the schedule and knowledge of their IT departments. This dramatically curtailed the spread of computing power across the enterprise as learning curves for using these machines remained steep and access to them remained tightly regulated.

Then in 1975, Micro Instrumentation and Telemetry Systems (MITS) released the first commercially successful pre-assembled microcomputer called the Altair 8800 (for the purist it was also available as a kit you built yourself). MITS founder Ed Roberts designed the machine which was based on the Intel 8080 microprocessor. He expected to sell only a few hundred units. However, upon the machine's release *Popular Electronics* ran an article about it and MITS received over a thousand orders in the first month alone. Obviously, a few thousand units would not merit the label of commercial success in today's market, but at the time it was groundbreaking.

The Altair's second claim to fame is that it drew the attention of two young programmers named Bill Gates and Paul Allen. These two future billionaires were impressed by the popularity of the 8800, so they contacted MITS and offered to demonstrate their version of a BASIC (Beginner's All-purpose Symbolic Instruction Code) Programming Language that could run on the new Altair machine and be used by software developers to create their own applications. When MITS agreed to a meeting, Allen flew to Albuquerque, New Mexico to demonstrate the programming language to Roberts and his team. In a harbinger of the millions of "blue screens" to come,[11] the demo was riddled with problems and included numerous code crashes, but Allen stuck with it and convinced MITS to sign a contract with him and Gates to distribute their Altair BASIC along with future sales of their microcomputers. Fresh on the heels of their new contract, the two young programmers promptly moved to New

---

[11] This is a reference to the fact that during the 1980s and 1990s Microsoft was notorious for selling products that were filled with bugs that caused computers to crash, resulting in the infamous "blue screen of death" in the Windows operating system.

Mexico and founded their own software company that they dubbed Microsoft.

By the late 1970s, pre-assembled, personal computers were beginning to proliferate, with companies like Tandy, Apple and Commodore among the first to begin mass-marketing. IBM took note of the growing market and became determined to continue its hegemony in every aspect of the computing market. After all, the company had been a major player in computing since the end of the 19th century when Herman Hollerith founded the company to produce his mechanical tabulator.

So in 1980, IBM prepared to once again assert itself as the undisputed leader in the computer market with the introduction of its new personal computer based on the more powerful Intel 8800 microprocessor. The IBM Personal Computer, or PC as it became universally known, was considered by some industry insiders to be a "miracle in a box." But this miracle didn't have the equivalent of a brain – which for a PC that meant an operating system or OS.

Of course, IBM could have gone through the trouble of writing one themselves, but at the time they considered themselves the ultimate hardware company. They had software to be sure, but the heart and soul of the company was big metal. And who could blame them. There are real barriers to entry to building a sophisticated piece of computing technology like a mainframe or a PC. In the late 1980s, I once heard a software development guy from IBM describe his role along the following lines: Being a software guy at IBM is like being the solar energy guy at Exxon. Everybody thinks it's a good idea, but no one takes you seriously.

Impressed with Microsoft's growing reputation in the microcomputer market, IBM reached out to Bill Gates to find out how they might make their upcoming PC better than any other on the market. One idea Gates floated by them was to have BASIC written directly into the computer's memory when it was sold. As part of their conversations, IBM noted they would need an operating system and inquired as to whether Microsoft would be willing to write one. Having never done so before, Gates demurred and suggested that IBM look to the company Digital Research and their operating system called CP/M (Control Program for Microcomputers) for a possible solution. Following Gates' advice, IBM reached out to CP/M's writer Gary Kindall in hopes of striking a quick deal. Kindall remarkably refused to sign a non-disclosure agreement with IBM, so rather than risk divulging any secrets of its upcoming miracle in a box, IBM returned to Gates and Microsoft.

This time Microsoft was awarded the contract to make a clone of CP/M to be the OS of the new IBM PC. Rather than start from scratch, they purchased the rights for an existing CP/M clone called QDOS, which stood for Quick and Dirty Operating System, from Seattle Computer Products for $70,000. They then improved the code and dubbed it MS-DOS for Microsoft Disk Operating System. Just like that, IBM had its operating system and Microsoft had stumbled into one of the most strategic positions in the demand data chain of a new and rapidly emerging market.

Almost from the moment of its introduction, IBM's PC set the pace for the entire market. Not only did the IBM machines capture significant market share, but the company spawned a large number of "clone" manufacturers that offered machines comparable to the IBM machines at ever decreasing prices. Household names like Dell and Gateway are just two of the long-term survivors of a savage competition for market share that started almost the day the IBM PC hit the market. Just as importantly, the IBM imprimatur gave large corporations the confidence to start spreading PCs to nearly every desk in the company. This was not insignificant because corporate leaders who had never even heard of a microcomputer were being asked to make huge financial outlays on unproven technologies and rather fuzzily defined benefits. In justifying these purchases, it was not uncommon to hear a popular saying of the time, "You can't get fired for buying IBM."

While IBM was busy selling and deploying PCs into every nook and cranny of corporations, they were also spreading the operating system of their partner Microsoft. As the OS spread, it created economic forces that would change the world.

The OS sits between a computer's hardware and the software that end users want to use. A computer requires all three components to be useful because a computer with just hardware and an OS is nothing more than an expensive and cumbersome paper weight. Therefore, useful software is the key to making a computer a good investment.

Despite this fact, software developers in the early 1980s were presented with a difficult challenge. The nascent microcomputer market was relatively small and to make matters worse, it was extremely fragmented. Therefore, if you wanted to write a software application, you had to decide which OS of the many available in the market you were targeting. It wasn't uncommon for software developers to have to keep multiple copies of their "source" code for the various OS platforms that they were trying to reach.

This made software applications difficult to develop and maintain, meaning high cost and low volume. In many ways, the PC industry prior to the IBM/Microsoft union was stuck in a chicken-and-egg negative feedback loop. Without much to offer in the way of software, it was difficult for hardware manufacturers and their respective OS to gain a large base of users. But without a large base of users to entice software developers, it was nearly impossible to get anyone to write software for your system.

Logically, the inverse of this problem is a positive feedback loop or a "virtuous cycle". This simply means that the more end users who use your hardware platform, the more software developers will want to write for your platform. And the more software that is available for your platform, the more end users will want to use your platform. Thus creating a virtuous cycle where more of one begets more of the other, over and over again.

The challenge to reaching this self fulfilling loop is to somehow create a critical mass on either side of the equation to prime the pump, if you will, and get the positive feedback loop moving forward. In the technology world this is known as a network effect. The more something gets used, the more valuable it becomes (positive network effect). This is contrary to most situations in the world where the more something gets used the less valuable it becomes (negative network effect). For example, the more cars are on any given stretch of highway, the less useful that stretch of highway becomes for everyone. Adding more cars will certainly not fix the problem.

On the flip side, what was the value of the first fax machine ever produced? Of course the answer is zero. If there is only one fax machine in the world, to whom are you going to send a fax? However, as each new fax machine is sold, the utility of your fax machine increases as you have an ever growing number of people to whom you can send a fax. This is a positive network effect and it holds for operating systems as much as it does for fax machines.

The IBM/Microsoft union created a critical mass of distribution that gave software developers a slightly larger market than all the other participants in the market. And as we will see throughout this book, small numerical advantages in demand can lead to huge implications for markets and profits.

In addition to IBM's sales muscle, Microsoft did a number of things right early on that allowed them to surpass Apple as the dominant operating system, even though DOS was considered inferior to Apple's OS on nearly every level. Apple's strategy was to control the entire process from software development to operating system mechanics to hardware production. Furthermore, Apple attempted to extract maximum value per unit sold and excluded the other participants in the value chain.

On the contrary, Microsoft sold their operating system for a very low price point, which made it attractive to IBM and others to install on their machines. Second, they reached out aggressively to the software developer community, the most innovative and creative of which were kids and hobbyists who couldn't afford the blood money demanded by Apple. Microsoft also offered free tools to developers to help them more efficiently write applications for DOS. All of this allowed Microsoft to tout the number of applications available in their OS as the primary reason you should buy machines loaded with it. And finally, Microsoft identified what applications it felt were most useful to PC users and helped those companies sell their software through joint marketing deals. In this, Microsoft had a huge advantage because MS-DOS came pre-loaded on the hardware. They could then offer to place a coupon or brochure of the software developer's products in the startup package of software with every new DOS machine sold.

All of these efforts, in conjunction with IBM's sales juggernaut created the critical mass to start the positive feedback cycle. The system began feeding on itself: more users = more software, more software = more users. From there it was a relatively short trip to the holy grail of a mystical place known in technology circles as network lockout.

This odd turn of phrase means that any technology system driven by a positive feedback loop creates certain powerful market forces. Once the loop reaches critical mass, future technologies, even if superior in many ways, will fail because they have to displace not just the feature set of the incumbent, but also the accumulated investment of all the participants in the system. This may sound a bit complicated, so perhaps a real world example might help to clarify it.

On a standard English language computer keyboard, the first six letters of the top row of keys, starting from left to right reads QWERTY. This particular arrangement of letters, as well as the placement of the rest of the letters on the keyboard, was designed with a specific purpose in mind – reduce the speed of the human typing on the keyboard. This may seem odd today, but there was a perfectly logical reason for wanting to retard the speed of keyboard users years ago.

Typewriters and the keyboards that came with them became commercially viable and popular in the mid 19th century. One of the key considerations given to early designs of the typewriter was the efficiency of the keyboard's arrangement. Originally typewriters were crafted so that the fastest typing fingers would strike the most commonly used letters. Oddly enough, this ended up creating a problem for typists. As anyone who has fumbled with an old typewriter knows, when a key is pressed a metal shaft with the imprint of a letter flies up and strikes an ink soaked ribbon, which in turn makes an imprint of the corresponding letter on the paper. In short order, people became more familiar with the keyboard and typing speeds climbed higher and higher. The problem came when a typist was too fast and the depression of one key would cause its metal shaft to rise towards the paper before the previous one had fully come down, resulting in the two rods jamming together. This became such a frequent problem that something had to be done.

In 1878 a man named Christopher Sholes patented his QWERTY keyboard. He had spent six years perfecting a keyboard whose letter placement was actually designed to slow typists down; the aim of doing so was to prevent or at least reduce key jams. The QWERTY keyboard quickly grew in popularity and by and large became an industry standard.

The early 1930s saw the beginnings of the electric typewriter and by the 1950s they were standard in most businesses. Unlike the earlier typewriters, an electric typewriter has no metal rods that can jam, and therefore the necessity for a keyboard that slows the typist down is no longer sensible. At this point, it would be reasonable to expect that some enterprising inventor would come up with a keyboard that was actually designed to speed up the typists, and you'd be right. Throughout the years, many differing models of keyboard have been introduced. But what kind of keyboard do you have at home? What about at your office? The QWERTY keyboard had become the standard and had "locked out" competing ideas.

Even though new keyboard designs were superior, everyone who knew how to type and every company that manufactured keyboards were all wedded to the QWERTY design. The new designs would have resulted in some incremental productivity gain for typists, but the global costs of retraining and retooling the industry far outweighed the value of those gains. So here we have an example of a clearly inferior design locking out a superior one simply because of critical mass.

The IBM/Microsoft combination was able to create a similar situation in the PC OS. Although Microsoft's design was in many ways inferior to other products from a technical perspective, it was superior in the all important fact that in a fairly short time frame it had more installed units and active users than any other OS in the market. In a rapidly changing and growing market, a period of punctuated equilibrium if you will, this proved to be crucial.

The small but significant lead MS-DOS was able to eke out led to what I call the ratchet. This is my way of describing what happens after some component of a rapidly growing and changing market gains some sort of informational advantage. In Microsoft's case, the slight advantage in the number of users registered with MS-DOS (again driven primarily by IBM's sales of its PC with the operating system pre-installed and not necessarily by the quality or superiority of Microsoft's design) was enough to prime the pump of the positive feedback loop that lead to network lockout.

The more users Microsoft acquired, the more software developers wanted to write for DOS. Think about it, if Microsoft has 30,000,000 users and Apple has 1,000,000, economically your chances of finding a market for your new software product are better with the larger user base. Furthermore, at the time Apple was charging fees for just about everything, making it extremely expensive for independent software developers, like my teenage self at the time, to afford to even consider writing for the Apple OS.

As more software becomes available, the more valuable buying a DOS PC becomes. Like the fax machine example described earlier, the more software applications that run in DOS, the more valuable it becomes to users, and the more users who use DOS, the more valuable it becomes to hardware and software developers. The system builds on itself by ratcheting back and forth between these two constituents until it reaches critical mass and network lockout.

The end result of this positive feedback loop was truly the Second Shock. It created a large market of computer users working on standardized hardware and software into which thousands of newly minted software developers, hackers, hobbyists and businesses could develop and sell software.

This created a massive win-win-win-win situation. Software developers won because the large standardized market meant their risk taking and hard work was now rewarded exponentially more so than it had ever been. Hardware manufacturers like IBM won because Microsoft was creating an enormous mass market for them as well. Microsoft won because, not only were they making a decent living with the relatively low cost OS, the lion's share of demand data they were amassing by becoming the de facto standard would come into play later in a huge way. And consumers won because they were getting a machine and an operating system that was growing in value with each new software application.

The fact that all of these new machines spreading from one end of the corporation to the other needed to be connected created another important factor that grew out of the rapidly growing PC market and would have a significant impact on the future. Digitized information was now being generated from every department, but if that information was not captured and shared efficiently, a large part of the value of computerizing the entire company would be lost.

Unlike the days of the mainframe and minicomputers where one processor was connected to several dumb terminals and stored all the data in a central repository, PCs were self contained machines that could store their own data. Furthermore, these new machines were designed to be used by everyone, not just highly trained experts. All of this meant companies were being forced to network hundreds and even thousands of computers. Initially, the idea was to tie together computers within close proximity to each other with the obvious moniker of Local Area Network, or LAN. Once this process was substantially completed, companies then began to integrate LANs together into a framework known as Wide Area Network, or WAN.

LANs and WANs integrated corporations in ways that had never existed before and established the technological foundations that would allow the commercialization of the Internet to zoom ahead in the mid-1990s. Companies like Novell rose to prominence through their innovations in connections that could easily move data across enterprises. Their networking created the new possibility of making computing highly valuable all the way out to the edges of the corporation and this in turn had huge economic impact in that more information could be captured, managed and utilized from every part of the company, not just the "gatekeepers" of a mainframe. All of a sudden it became much easier to capture and store information from marketing and sales and other customer-facing systems.

As digital information pushed to the edges of the corporation, a growing concern arose over the security of those networks. This in turn brought about the barriers around networks that became known as "firewalls". A firewall is the part of a computer network that blocks unauthorized access to a network while allowing authorized actions and communications. The firewall became the digital line of demarcation between a company and the outside world with very little information being shared between firewalled entities.

This was primarily attributable to security concerns, but similar to the early days of the fragmented OS market, there was no standard protocol for getting different brands of networking software to talk to each other. This would all change with the Third Shock, but the efforts to wire entire organizations constituted a major change in the way businesses looked at and interacted with the world around them.

Chapter IV: The Third Shock: The Internet and the Web

"During my service in the United States Congress, I took the initiative in creating the Internet."
-   Al Gore, March 9, 1999

This may come as a surprise to some of you but Al Gore did not invent the Internet. Like the two previous shocks, the Internet did not happen overnight. When most people think of the Internet as a creation of the 1980s and 1990s, they are thinking of the time when it began to impact the world economy at large, but the Internet is significantly older than that.

The Internet had its start in the early 1960s, so considering that Al Gore served in the US House of Representatives from 1976-1984 and the U.S. Senate from 1984 to 1992, his comment from early 1999 was unmercifully ridiculed by his political opponents and late night TV hosts. Of course, those comments were taken out of context and Gore attempted to respond to the criticism with a bit of humor. The day before an interview with CNN's Wolf Blitzer later that year, Gore said, "The day I made that statement, about inventing the Internet, I was tired because I'd been up all night inventing the Camcorder." However, the truth of the matter is pretty well summed up in the following excerpt from Wired Magazine:

"...while Gore certainly didn't create the Internet, he was one of the first politicians to realize that those bearded, bespectacled researchers were busy crafting something that could, just maybe, become pretty important.

In January 1994, Gore gave a landmark speech at UCLA about the "information superhighway".

Many portions -- discussions of universal service, wiring classrooms to the Net, and antitrust actions -- are surprisingly relevant even today. (That's an impressive enough feat that we might even forgive Gore his tortured metaphors such as "road kill on the information superhighway" and "parked at the curb" on the information superhighway.)

Gore's speech reverberated around Democratic political circles in Washington. Other Clinton administration officials began citing it in their own remarks, and the combined effort helped to grab the media's attention.

Their timing was impeccable: In July 1993, according to Network Wizards' survey, there were 1.8 million computers connected to the Internet. By July 1994, the figure had nearly doubled to 3.2 million, a trend that continued through January 2000, when about 72 million computers had permanent network addresses."[12]

> The Mother of Gore's Invention, Declan McCullagh in the October 17, 2000 issue of Wired Magazine

The real story of the Internet starts in 1962 when the U.S. Department of Defense's Advanced Research Projects Agency named J.C.R. Licklider to be its head. As one of the earliest proponents of the creation of some sort of global network, Licklider immediately began working on research to bring it to fruition. His first step was to build a network of three terminals for the exchange of information across the country. One was in Santa Monica; one was in Berkeley, and the third was in Cambridge at MIT. One of Licklider's main frustrations with his little three node network was that he could only communicate with one node at a time through a fixed connection. If he were online with

---

[12] As of this writing Internetworldstats.com lists the active number of Internet users in the world today at approximately 1.5 billion.

The Fourth Shock

Cambridge, the only way he could communicate with his peers in Berkeley would be to get up from one terminal and move to a different one to start a conversation. This got him thinking about a way to design a network that would allow everyone to connect through a single terminal.

This idea spawned the first incarnation of one of the networks that would become the Internet – ARPANET (Advanced Research Projects Agency Network). ARPANET originally connected a node on the campus of UCLA to the Stanford Research Center in late October of 1969. By early December, two more nodes had been added to the network at the University of Utah and the University of California at Santa Barbara. From that success, new nodes, or hosts, were added fairly rapidly, and around a decade later the number of ARPANET hosts had surpassed 200.

A key component of Licklider's idea was his incorporation of the concept of using "packet switching" to move information rather than single fixed connection. Before packet switching, the method of communicating was "message switching", in which data was transported in its entirety. Packet switching is a form of communicating on a network in which a data stream is broken down into individual pieces, or packets, to be transmitted in easier to manage sections than if the data was transmitted whole. The breaking down of digitized information into packets increased the efficiency of network links exponentially and allowed for simultaneous communication by all members of the network.

The Fourth Shock

Once the packet switching concept began to be utilized successfully by ARPANET, different private networks sprung up around the world. One of the more successful network protocols to arise was X.25, which used packet switching but modeled its data transmission on the same formation as telephone communication, only using virtual circuits. Unlike ARPANET that remained the province of the defense industry and related academic institutions, X.25 was actually available for common business use. Therefore, throughout the '70s and early '80s it was used to start a number of networks, such as the British JANET, the International Packet Switched Service, Telenet, and CompuServe. Importantly, CompuServe became the first to offer email to personal computers.

As networking grew in popularity, it was clear that the time was coming to truly fulfill Licklider's dream of one merged, global network, and the folks over at ARPANET put a man named Vinton Cerf in charge of the effort. What Cerf and his colleagues came up with was a sort of restructuring, in which aspects that made each network fundamentally different from another were hidden by a common Internetwork protocol, not too dissimilar in concept to Microsoft's DOS. Also in the earlier versions of ARPANET, the network itself was responsible for its own reliability, but with the potential size of a mass combination of networks, they decided that it would be best to make the individual hosts responsible. In 1974, Cerf and his team wrote up a protocol document called "RFC 75" (requests for comments) where the term Internet was first used (two years before Al Gore was elected to the US House of Representatives). In what would prove to be an important moment for the future, RFC 75 defined the Internet as any network using the TCP/IP standards set forth in the document a.k.a. Transmission Control Protocol and Internet Protocol.

Over the next ten years numerous organizations and companies adopted the TCP/IP framework and it slowly started its long climb to a positive feedback loop and its position as a global networking standard. In the mid-1980s and into the early 1990s there were still some networks, mainly in Europe, that used their own forms of networking and were disjointed from the growing Internet. Also, most companies in the US and elsewhere still had internal networks that were based on proprietary standards that required converters and adapters to connect those to TCP/IP. However, throughout the late '80s the use of TCP/IP continued to gain in popularity and began to penetrate eastward from Europe and into Asia.

One of the key factors driving the Internet's expansion was the rapidly growing use of email. As greater and greater stores of information were being interconnected on the Internet, it became clear that there needed to be some way of storing and searching files on the increasingly large network. The introduction of hypertext seemed to resonate with Internet users as the preferred form of navigation due to its simplicity and functionality. This allowed text to be linked to just about any other text or objects on the Internet. A user simply clicked on the link to jump to the highlighted text. While the concept was a hit with tech savvy users of the Internet, the lack of a standardized tagging language or procedure made it difficult to add links for anyone less than an expert. Tackling this problem became the focus of a man named Tim Berners-Lee who introduced a new network-based hypertext protocol called the World Wide Web.

Berners-Lee originally came up with the concept of the World Wide Web (the Web) in 1990 and introduced it in 1991. The Web, as most readers are now aware, is a collection of information, documents, images, and other resources on the Internet that can be navigated using links. The breakthrough idea that allowed him to merge hypertext with the Internet was something called Hyper Text Markup Language, or more commonly HTML. HTML is the code language of the Internet that allows for the linking of all those different documents, images and other information on the Web.

As HTML began to capture the imagination of the early Internet pioneers, the push to make the Web increasingly more user friendly began to take hold. Specifically, it became clear that the extensive coding of information with HTML was creating an interesting new way of navigating through information, but what was lacking was a user friendly interface for that navigation. Therefore, the next great step forward was the development of what today is universally known as the "browser."

A Web browser is a software application for presenting information on the Web and navigating through it. In 1993, the National Center for Supercomputing Applications (NCSA) released their browser called Mosaic free to the world. Among its many neat features, Mosaic made it relatively easy to display text and graphics on the same page. It was not the most powerful or efficient way of surfing the web, but it was the most user-friendly. Its clean and easily navigated interface caused a sudden and mostly unexpected explosion of interest in the Web. This single application is often cited as the catalyst that started the positive feedback loop that ended with the Internet spreading across the globe.

Despite its importance, Mosaic's reign was short-lived. Typically, as the interest in the Web swelled and an ever expanding base of users logged on to the Net, entrepreneurs and their venture capitalist enablers weren't far behind. One of the first and most important of these combinations of brains and money came from a fairly odd couple.

The team leader for the development of the NCSA's Mosaic was a student named Marc Andreessen. After graduating from college, he moved to California and quickly met Silicon Valley stalwart Jim Clark. Clark had recently left Silicon Graphics, a successful technology company he had founded, and was searching for his next big thing. Along the way he had stumbled upon Mosaic and grew convinced that the browser had great commercial possibilities. He sought out Andreessen and convinced him to join him as cofounder and vice president of technology for the Mosaic Communications Corporation.

The Fourth Shock

After complaints from the University of Illinois about the use of the Mosaic name, the company rechristened itself Netscape Communications, and shortly thereafter launched the Netscape Navigator, its flagship Web browser in 1994. Andreessen was 23 years old.

Netscape Navigator made its debut in 1994 and was available free for non-commercial use. It also had some significant improvements over Mosaic – the foremost of which being the ability to display text and images on a web page while it was loading. Previous browsers would have to load the entire page before any of it could be viewed.

On the strength of its neat new features, Netscape quickly became the standard browser for Windows users. This in turn propelled it towards a speedy IPO. However, this IPO was unlike any the world had ever seen before. In August of 1995, the company was poised to be listed on the NASDAQ market at an initial offering price of $14 per share. On the advice of their investment bankers, Netscape doubled its offering at the last minute and the shares began trading that day at $28 per share. By the end of the day the shares closed at $75 per share, marking one of the largest first day gains in history. The company, which had never posted a significant profit and had $16.0 million in trailing twelve month revenue, ended the day with a market capitalization of $2.2 billion. On December 5, the stock peaked at $171 per share, making Jim Clark's 32% stake in the company worth over $1 billion.

Netscape remained the standard browser for Windows users for a period of time, that is until Microsoft decided to enter the market with their own browser called Internet Explorer and used their information advantage to crush them.

Although Netscape's lead would dissipate rather quickly, the IPO mania it ignited did not. As *Time* magazine noted, IPOs for high-tech companies generated over $8.0 billion in new capital in 1995 compared to $29 billion for all industries during the same period. To say this got the attention of the entire world is an extreme understatement.

Suddenly CEO's of "brick and mortar" companies who had never touched a computer in their entire lives were hammering their executives to come up with an Internet strategy. The following years were a period of economic frenzy rarely seen in modern history. Greed and fear gripped the economy and everyone tried to get in on the act with varying degrees of success.

In spite of what Federal Reserve Chairman Alan Greenspan in 1996 famously termed "irrational exuberance," the Internet bubble did accelerate the TCP/IP protocol's acceptance as the networking standard of the world. And this is the first component of the Third Shock – an international and near universal standard for networking.

This in turn allowed companies and organizations to more easily integrate their internal networks with the other partners in their supply chain. Initially, companies were reasonably concerned about two aspects of using the Internet as a means to extend their internal information systems through their own firewall to integrate with partners and customers.

First and foremost was security. Once information left the secure confines of a company's firewall, businesses were very wary of potential breaches of confidential information. A second concern was reliability. If companies were going to connect to partners via the Internet, mission critical business processes had to be reliable. However, it wasn't too long before even these reasonable objections to using the TCP/IP protocol were overcome and the full impact of the Third Shock would be felt.

The Third Shock is simply the integration of supply chains and vendors across industries using a standard protocol. Much like the standardized operating system of the '80s allowed computing to push all the way to the edges of the enterprise, the standardized Internet protocol, an abstraction layer of various other protocols, allowed information to be pushed through the firewall to extend the enterprise to all parts of the value chain – customers, partners, suppliers etc.

The world we live in today, with a global network able to zip information to any point at the speed of light has changed the way businesses look at themselves and their relationship to their customers, partners and competitors. By extending the enterprise beyond the limits of the firewall, new efficiencies were wrung from the integration of existing supply chains.

And like Microsoft DOS before it, network effects are what prodded the Internet to this universality. Was IP the best networking protocol that has ever or will ever exist? Probably not. But that's irrelevant. What is relevant is that it became the standard. It was another virtuous cycle: the more companies that used IP, the more IP became valuable to all those agreeing to use the standard. The more IP became valuable, the more other companies wanted to switch to IP.

One of the most important changes caused by the Third Shock was the way companies viewed the relationship with their consumers. Companies all over the world became exponentially more reactive to demand data at the customer level. Think about it. In the days of the mainframe and the First Shock era, what did a business react to? Inventory and accounting data, all of which is completely reactive in nature. Then with the Second Shock, when the technology was pushed out to the edges of the corporation in the 1980s and 1990s, companies began gathering and reacting to information at the edges of the corporation – sales information, customer facing systems, digitized call centers and the like. The volume of information about the state of the market increased exponentially, but it was still reactive in nature. An employee on the network could offer information just learned from a meeting with a customer, and that information could be driven across the organization into the right hands and acted upon. But in the Third Shock, the consumers *themselves*, business partners and other contributors to the value chain can interact with a company in real-time anywhere on the globe. It was the logical conclusion of the ideal reactive system. What did we learn from our partners? Let's do something. What did we learn from our point-of-sale data, or from our partner's point-of-sales systems? Let's do something. Sell something, do something.

This continual evolution of the information supply chain, from the isolated, ivory towers of the First Shock's mainframes through the integration of information systems across the enterprise in the Second Shock, to the extension of those information systems across enterprises in the Third, has created the foundation for a whole new dynamic in the way businesses will interact with the world.

Unlike all of these efforts to date which have focused on capturing information closer and closer to the point-of-sale and reacting to it to streamline production, the Fourth Shock ushers in the era where demand data *before* a sale is made becomes the key to future competitiveness. To be clear, the fact that there are over 4 billion active cell phone accounts in the world today is not the Fourth Shock. Mobility has been around for a long time. Many of us can remember Michael Douglas' character Gordon Gekko in the 1987 film *Wall Street* walking up and down the beach talking into a cell phone the size of a small refrigerator. That was mobility in action over 20 years ago.

To be sure, mobility's time has come because the technology infrastructure is in place, the potential market is enormous, consumer behavior is conditioned to the point of being comfortable with the technology, and the power and value of capturing demand data ahead of competitors is proven.

The Fourth Shock, like the three previous shocks, is not about technology but rather the point when a disruptive technology forces changes in the way businesses see themselves and their relationship to the world at large. It is specifically about the all important value of capturing real-time demand data and reacting to it before competitors and even other participants in the supply chain. Mobile devices will play a tremendous part in the Fourth Shock because they are creating new types of real-time demand information that will be used by companies to create unprecedented value, but they are only part of the equation.

However, unlike the three previous shocks, the Fourth Shock is about being proactive rather than reactive. The rest of this book explores the impact of capturing proactive demand data in order to gain an informational advantage and to then use it to create extraordinary profits over extended periods of time.

PART II

The Fourth Shock:
Demand

Data

Dominance

Chapter V: What We Can All Learn from Enron

Once I rose above the noise and confusion
Just to get a glimpse beyond this illusion,
I was soaring ever higher,
But I flew too high.

- Kansas, Carry On My Wayward Son

Enron? Seriously? I can almost hear your mind recoiling in disgust as it digests the title of this chapter. What could I possibly want to learn about excessive greed, deceit, fraud, failure and criminal activity, and what could any of that have to do with the future of the global economy? Actually, quite a bit. Too often human nature tends to make us turn away from business crimes the size and scope of Enron and dismiss the whole experience as a brief period of corporate madness. However, if you are willing to look a little deeper and keep an open mind, you will see that the rise and fall of Enron holds many lessons for nearly every business in the world today.

Obviously, Enron Corporation deserves its disgrace. Arrogant executives, financial deceit and one of the largest bankruptcies in history serve as a cautionary reminder to all of us that what goes up almost always must come down. However, like a modern day Icarus, it was the lofty heights achieved by Enron that made its plummet so spectacular. If Enron had been a small enterprise rather than the 7th largest company in America, few of us would have taken note of it despite the criminal behavior of its executives. This spectacular implosion obscures the fact that Enron did not begin life as a corporate giant and media darling that year-in and year-out was listed as one of the world's most respected companies. On the contrary, Enron had a fairly humble beginning. So what did the company do right in the early days that allowed it to claw its way to the top of the capitalist system, and what *really* caused it to end up on the trash heap of historical infamy?

Much has been written about Enron's famous fall by academics and pundits, but little has been written about what made the company worthy of our attention in the first place. Most of the books and articles on Enron's collapse center around the argument that Enron's demise was caused by the aforementioned hubris, fraud and criminal behavior, and in a way of course they are correct. However, this line of reasoning is akin to arguing that someone's life is a mess because he is a drug addict, whereas the more likely case is that he is addicted to drugs because his life was already a mess. It is a case of inverting causality, and in many ways the same can be said for much of the perceived common wisdom about Enron. The fraud and criminal behavior didn't cause the fall of Enron – although the excessive arrogance may have had a huge hand in it – but rather these actions were brought about by a company that was already failing. Furthermore, what was causing it to fail was a lack of the very thing that made them so successful in the first place – *proprietary, real-time demand data.*

Enron's sins and sinners have completely overshadowed the business practices that initially thrust them into the spotlight and allowed them to create staggering rates of return on investments for over a decade.[13] Enron rose to corporate prominence by looking at newly deregulated industries in a very unique way. They recognized early on that when an industry is in flux from a supply/demand perspective, the opportunity to maximize profitability lies in getting and using an informational advantage on one or both sides of the equation. Enron, that infamous blemish on American capitalism, was a pioneer in understanding that the demand information embedded in transactions was often worth more than the transaction itself. Allow me to explain.

---

[13] Author of *Enron: the Rise and Fall* Loren Fox recounts that Ernon's revenue in 1987 was $5.9 billion. According to the company's financial statement a year before its demise, Enron's 2000 revenue was $101 billion.

The Fourth Shock

Enron's history began in 1985 with the seemingly mundane merger of InterNorth, Inc. based in Omaha, Nebraska, and the Houston Natural Gas Company. Few people would have guessed that this new entity would quickly become one of the largest companies in America. Six months after the merger, the company changed its name from the brutally uncreative moniker of HNG/InterNorth to the now notorious Enron. Driven by the diminutive Ken Lay, whose ego and ambitions were anything but, and his future wunderkind protégé Jeffry Skilling, Enron began an assault on business models that would change the way the entire global economy works.

Within a few months of the merger, Ken Lay had maneuvered the newly constituted board of the combined company into accepting a plan to make him the CEO despite the fact that his company, HNG, was significantly smaller than InterNorth. He also began laying the groundwork for the company to be headquartered in Houston rather than Omaha, rolling over objections and resentment from the InterNorth board members and stakeholders. Lay knew that in order to fully capitalize on the new company's strategic position he would need to be at the epicenter of the American energy industry.

These strategic advantages were not insignificant. The company boasted a value of $12 billion, and more importantly controlled 37,500 miles of gas pipelines making it the largest gas-distribution system in the country. With pipelines spanning from coast to coast, the new company had access to California, Texas, and Florida, the three largest and fastest growing gas markets in the country.

Perhaps the greatest strategic advantage however would be found in the way Lay looked at the value of these assets. To him, a gas pipeline was really a means of understanding information flows about demand for natural gas. Gas went in one end and came out the other. And if you could be the first one to know how much demand was being created at the consumption side, you could use that information to make money from the production side and vice versa. But in order to do so, you would have to essentially invert the industry's business model.

At the time of Enron's creation, the United States government set the market price for natural gas. On the surface, this was a great deal for natural gas consumers as prices were kept artificially low for political purposes. On the flip side, this situation presented natural gas producers and the pipeline companies that moved the gas from the fields to the consumers with two significant problems. First, the fixed price discouraged aggressive development of new natural gas fields. Once the most accessible gas fields were producing, the added costs of finding and developing new natural gas supplies in ever more remote locales was simply not cost effective. This had obvious implications for the supply of gas. Second, what many people tend to forget, including most politicians, is that in a free market, price is not just a means to profitability. It also conveys tremendously valuable information to producers and consumers alike about the relative position of supply and demand. A consistently high price in a free market indicates to producers that they can take additional risk to produce more of the good or service. On the other hand, it signals to consumers to either cut back on consumption and/or find alternative ways of getting the same results.

Because price was not a reliable demand signal, producers were blind to how much gas they should be producing to meet real market needs. And so, like many other commodity based industries, gas producers and pipeline companies attempted to use "trading" activities to hedge against production risk. By entering into long-term contracts called "futures", producers could sell future production today and glean some idea as to how much they need to produce or transport. However, a fixed price on the consumer end meant that the price volatility within the market was relatively low and therefore, gas consumers were not terribly interested in signing counterparty agreements because they could always buy gas at the same price. This meant trading activities were a valuable but relatively small part of gas production and pipeline companies' overall activities.

At the time, Enron was no different than most of the other participants in the market. However, as the owner of the largest natural gas pipeline, Enron was in a unique position to view more of the entire market and glean insights as to the true nature of demand as they watched the gas ebb and flow through their pipes. Furthermore, Enron was betting that eventually gas prices would be deregulated and when that happened they would have a distinct informational advantage over other participants in the market.

In 1981 newspapers blared the following headline: "Schools Close to Avert Natural Gas Shortage."[14] This was followed throughout the early 1980s with various gas shortage issues slamming the economy and causing politicians and regulators no small amount of embarrassment. A number of remedial steps were taken to stimulate supply and curtail demand, but the writing was on the wall and by the late 1980s, the natural gas market was well on its way to being deregulated. As is often the case, politicians eventually learned that it is better to allow the chaotic yet efficient forces of the free market to take the credit and blame for supply and demand and the resultant prices rather than government regulators (see: the Soviet Union).

With gas prices rapidly marching towards deregulation, Enron began betting that the volatility in the natural gas market would rise dramatically. In the gas trading world, volatility simply means the amount of change in price that can be experienced or expected for a gas contract over a given time frame. The question at the time running through the rapidly expanding company was simple: "What will deregulation mean for Enron?" As Ken Lay pondered the question, the answer wasn't obvious. However, an experience in the late 1980s had given him a taste of the riches to be gained from trading activities as well as the

---

[14] The Bryan Times, January 16, 1981

risks. In correspondence to colleagues at the time, Lay clearly indicated that not only could Enron weather the storms of change, the company may be able to take advantage of these changes to greatly expand its profitability.

Shortly after the creation of Enron in 1985, a shining star quickly emerged from the smorgasbord of subsidiaries – Enron Oil & Gas. EOG as it was commonly known, was Enron's oil production and trading division with offices in Valhalla, New York. In the second year after the HNG/InterNorth merger, the oil traders at EOG netted the company $28 million – a greatly appreciated sum for a company that in almost all other areas was losing money and struggling to gain its footing. This tidy profit appeared to many of the executives in Houston as money from Heaven. By simply using information and trading futures contracts, the company was able to generate real profits. This definitely had an impact on Lay and the other executives, one of whom sent a message at the time to EOG's chief saying, "You understand your business better than anyone else alive…Please keep making us millions."[15]

Unfortunately for Enron, the high times for the oil traders did not last. In October of 1987 the man who had started EOG, Louis Borget, sat down with Ken Lay's number two in command Mick Seidl and gave a desperate confession. For months, Borget and EOG had been betting

---

[15] Bethany McLean and Peter Elkind, *The Smartest Guys in the Room*, p. 20

oil prices would go down. But prices had steadily done the opposite. Stubbornly hoping the market would turn back their way, the traders at EOG had finally dug a hole that was too deep to continue. Borget had also been ignoring trading limits that were supposed to keep traders from sinking the firm, with the result being that EOG now faced over $1 billion in potential losses. This situation, combined with the struggling company's debt still held over from the merger threatened Enron with bankruptcy.

In crisis mode, Enron sent the head of the liquid fuels division Mike Muckleroy, who had experience in commodities trading, to New York. Muckleroy promptly dismissed Borget. Then he and his disaster recovery crew proceeded to bluff the markets long enough for oil prices to drop to a point where it was feasible to close EOG's positions. The resultant $140 million in losses was hardly chump change, but at least Enron would be able to avoid bankruptcy.

The EOG saga forced the company to reevaluate its trading practices, and in this near-death experience the seeds of Enron's future were sown. While the situation at EOG did blow up in their faces, it had two positive effects on senior management and in particular Lay: 1) it demonstrated the money making power of trading activities, and 2) it underscored the risks inherent in not having the best trading systems and controls in place for those activities. Bottom line: if you were going to use trading activities to generate profits rather than simply hedge against production risks, you had better do it right.

The Fourth Shock

From that point forward the company embarked on a significant upgrade of its trading systems and focused on getting the right information to the right person at the right time – both from a trading perspective and from a compliance and control perspective. These investments would put Enron ahead of the curve when it came time to apply its trading systems and the lessons learned to the natural gas market, where they would have a continual supply of unique demand information – something that was lacking in the EOG trading operations.

Around the same time Enron was struggling to digest the lessons of EOG, a brilliant young executive named Jeffrey Skilling joined the firm. By 1991, Skilling had maneuvered his way to head the two fastest growing divisions of Enron – Enron Finance and Enron Gas Services – and merged them into a new entity dubbed Enron Capital & Trade, or ECT. On the surface, this looks like an odd combination of subsidiaries. What could Gas Services and Finance have to do with each other?

Enron Finance's stated purpose was to enable an innovative form of trading around gas distribution that Skilling believed would be more efficient in capturing profit on both sides of the pipeline transaction. Enron Gas Services was the arm of the company that dealt with finding customers willing to sign up for long-term gas contracts. The union of these two units into a new kind of company – *one that combined the information flows of the gas supply business with the money making potential of trading activities* – would become the foundation for the company's unprecedented growth in the coming years and clearly showed that Enron was starting to view its business differently than the rest of the gas distribution market. As early as 1991, Enron was pretty much betting the ranch that the natural gas market would be fully deregulated in the near future. Furthermore, it shows that the company intended to use its dominant position in gas distribution and its new-found understanding of trading activities to invert the business model of the entire natural gas industry. Namely - rather than use trading activities as merely a hedge against production risks, Enron would use production - which in their case meant gas transmission *and the information embedded in that activity* - as a hedge against trading risk.

Sure enough, after decades of efforts from a wide variety of interested parties, the natural gas industry was finally deregulated in 1993 and Enron was ready to pounce. There were no longer government-enforced contracts delineating the way producers, pipelines, and customers would interact with each other, and the natural gas industry became subject to the immutable laws of supply and demand.

Markets, almost by definition, often seem chaotic in their behavior as the individual choices of the numerous participants inexorably, yet almost mysteriously, settle on the constantly evolving equilibrium point of supply and demand. However, in a newly deregulated market, this chaos, or in market terms, volatility is extremely pronounced. In the period immediately following deregulation, the numerous competing participants are often unsure how to efficiently achieve their goals as they struggle to understand the brave new world in which they find themselves. Once the government stopped setting natural gas prices, markets were free to fluctuate at the whims of factors as mutable as the weather. A sudden cold spell in one part of the country could drive up demand for gas used to heat homes and businesses, and thus gas prices rose in a matter of minutes. Literally overnight, a frustratingly slow market held down by government intervention became a frighteningly real-time market that could turn on a dime.

It was in this newly deregulated and unstable industry that Enron would rise to global prominence. The experiences of Enron Oil & Gas had forced the company to invest heavily in their trading systems, and this would prove to be a boon in the emerging market. In addition, the company owned the largest gas pipeline in the country which gave them *unique and proprietary* demand information about a meaningful percentage of the overall market. Although each producer could know how much demand they were seeing, Enron had the benefit of moving gas from many producers and could therefore aggregate this information to gain more meaningful insights into overall market demand. But their biggest advantage was found in their audacious notion of using production to offset trading risk. While every other participant would use the information flowing from trading activities to adjust production, Enron would use the information flowing from their pipelines to maximize the value of their trading activities. In order to accomplish this *inversion* of the business model, Skilling needed a more institutionalized approach to capturing and leveraging demand information for profit.

In the early years following deregulation, 75% of all natural gas sales in the country were traded on the spot market within the last few days of each month. A spot market is a market in which the commodity is sold for cash and delivered immediately. At the end of each month a frantic flurry of activity would erupt on commodity markets with producers, pipelines, and consumers all trying to lock in last minute prices for gas that would be in their respective interests for the following month.

This dependence on last minute contracts created a very volatile market. Large natural gas customers and producers were forced to make the best decisions they could, but they were never completely sure they would be protected from significant price swings throughout the month. Eventually, both producers and consumers looked to the pipeline companies, as the middlemen, to take the risk of guaranteeing a long-term price.

Skilling was glad to oblige, but not for the reasons that other pipelines did. He recognized early on that the best way to exploit the current market situation and maximize Enron's strengths was to essentially turn ECT into a market maker for natural gas. He saw that on one side of the market were consumers who did not know what production really looked like, and on the other side were producers who had no idea what demand looked like. And Enron happened to be sitting right in the middle of them.

Skilling realized that if Enron could gather more information than just a single gas producer or gas consumer, that informational advantage would allow them to exploit the apprehensions of all the other participants in the market. And of course, Enron's position as the largest pipeline could facilitate the gathering of the information that would lead to that advantage. After all, Enron knew how much gas was in their pipes. They could constantly see how much was going out to their customers. So why not use that information to capture value on both sides of the transaction in addition to simply getting paid to move the gas through their pipes?

Skilling's brainchild to do all of this was something he dubbed the "Gas Bank". In this system, Enron would simply form a contract to *simultaneously* buy gas from a producer and sell that gas to a consumer. It was essentially a risk free transaction for Enron. And because they were in the unique position to more fully understand the overall supply and demand situation better than any other participant in the transaction, the spread between what they paid for the gas and what they sold it for was far greater than spreads that could be achieved in the frantic spot markets of the day.

The brilliance of this system was its originality, simplicity, and singularity. As the Gas Bank increased in popularity and moved ever increasing amounts of gas, Enron's informational advantage grew as well. While other companies were employing traditional methods of gathering supply and demand data and using in-house trading activities to hedge against price swings, Enron went full circle. They began using real-time demand data – a resource to which their unique position in the Gas Bank system gave them unparalleled access – to profit from every aspect of the supply chain, not just transmission. They were making money from parts of the supply chain that had always been seen as, at best, cost-neutralizing centers. And this is why Enron consistently outperformed its rivals. Rather than get paid merely for moving gas, it used its pipelines as a sophisticated device for capturing real-time supply and demand information and used that information to profit across the supply chain.

It is an inversion of the business model and the implications are profound. Think about it, after a certain point, adding additional pipelines would have only had a marginal impact on Enron's profitability. By simply capturing the information in its existing pipelines and applying that information to trading activities, Enron was able to consistently generate significantly higher rates of profitability from the same set of assets, essentially capturing profits or savings within the supply chain that would have normally been realized by the producers or consumers. Those same old pipelines that for years were barely breaking even suddenly became a vehicle for consistently producing huge profits and propelled an unknown company to the top of the capitalist system.

Skilling and Enron weren't done innovating there. They added exotic ideas such as derivatives based on the contracts already in the Gas Bank, further allowing them to reduce risk and lock in profits. In a basic sense, they were legally cheating. But a cynic could argue that they simply got lucky – right place, right assets, right technology, right people, all at the right time. Then they duplicated everything in another market.

By 1994, ECT was effectively dominating natural gas trading from each end of the supply chain, but the ambitions of Lay and Skilling would not be appeased by one massive market. They believed their ability to dominate trading in the gas market could be replicated in other markets. So in that year, ECT set its sights on the electricity markets. Like natural gas a year earlier, electricity was being deregulated, and ECT was certain it would undergo the same types of inefficiencies, and hence opportunities, as the gas markets.

So in 1994, ECT began electricity trading operations. The ever-confident Skilling placed his top lieutenants in charge of the new unit and awaited the inevitable profit avalanche. What could go wrong? Skilling was convinced he had seen this movie before – a newly deregulated market with unsophisticated participants would surely be cut to pieces by Enron's awesome technological lead in trading systems and the best and brightest traders in the world. He even mused publicly about creating a global company with no physical assets.

Unfortunately, something happened on the way to electricity market dominance – or more accurately, nothing happened. Despite Enron's best efforts, the new unit was not getting the same traction that the gas trading operations had seen years earlier. But reminiscent of the Enron Oil & Gas experience and under Lay's guidance, Enron simply retrenched. It was at this moment that the entire business model apparently fell into place – in order to consistently win in the upside down world of trading first, production second, you need access to proprietary demand information. You must know where a market is headed before the other participants and act on that information quickly. Without this key ingredient, billion dollar trading systems can only get so far because eventually other market participants will build similar systems and effectively chase away your advantage. Continuous access to proprietary real-time demand data is another story altogether. This is the key piece of the puzzle that allowed Enron to generate superior and consistent profits in the gas business and they simply had no equivalent in electricity. Somehow, Enron needed to insinuate itself between supply and demand and be the first to understand their relative relationship in order to turn the corner to sustained profitability in the electricity market.

Fundamentally, Enron needed to find the equivalent of its pipeline network in the electricity market. However, unlike natural gas, electricity cannot be stored efficiently, so once it is generated it needs to be transmitted. This meant that owning the transmission lines – which would be the closest physical parallel to its gas pipelines – was not feasible as there was no way to act on informational advantages in the power lines because electricity delivery was virtually instantaneous. However, studying the supply chain a bit further yielded a viable alternative – own the power plants themselves.

Although this went against Skilling's almost now-fanatical belief that physical assets were at best a necessary evil, it was the logical point in the supply chain to capture a consistent supply of demand data. In essence, a power plant is a fairly straight forward yet sophisticated machine. In one side goes fuel used to generate heat which is used to create steam that in turn spins a turbine.[16] Out of the other end of the spinning turbine comes electricity.

Profits in a power plant come from the differential in the price you can get for the electricity generated minus the cost of the fuel inputs and operations. In the industry this is known as the "spark spread". Enron recognized that much like the pipeline function in the gas market, a power plant is the ideal choke point for sensing real-time changes in demand. If, like Enron, you know what to do with that information, you can make gobs of money across the supply chain. Therefore, in 1997 Enron completed the acquisition of Portland General Electric Company, a major electricity provider in the Pacific Northwest.

As we say in Louisiana, from that point forward it was laissez les bon temps roulez. By 2000, Enron was the world's largest trader of natural gas and electricity and was rapidly expanding globally. Lightning had struck twice and the egos of Lay and Skilling were reaching epic heights.

---

[16] Of course, a hydro-electric plant turns the turbine by controlling the flow of water.

The only question on Skilling's mind was what to do for an encore. The incredible success of the past 10 years had convinced him that Enron's immense investment in trading technology and brains could be applied to virtually any industry with impunity. Once again he seemed to dismiss the value of physical assets and the need for sustainable access to real-time demand data in favor of trading prowess, despite the lessons of the electricity trading unit. He and Enron became too big to fail in his own mind.

From that point forward Skilling unleashed his ambitions on the world, simultaneously attacking an ever-growing list of industries with Enron's inverted business model strategy. Water, chemicals, metals, computer storage, weather trading; the list goes on and on. The company made a few half-hearted attempts to buy physical assets in some of these, but Skilling was convinced that his trading system was the best in the world and no longer needed the physical assets to be successful.

He couldn't have been more wrong. Over the next two years the far flung operations and trading activities of the firm began to underperform. In hindsight it is clear that the real source of Enron's stellar performance was combining real-time proprietary demand data with world class trading operations to squeeze profits out of the entire supply chain, but Skilling's over confidence and godlike hubris would not let him admit a mistake. Unlike the years when Lay was at the helm and Enron stumbled only to step back and retrench, Skilling charged mercilessly forward. As his dream world crumbled around him, he resorted to chicanery and fraud. This brought about the sad end to Enron.

The lessons for the world in the Enron debacle can be summed up in the following statement: Enron thrived by combining a continuous supply of proprietary demand data with world class trading operations and strategies to capture value across the supply chain. Conversely, they failed when they did not have access to demand data.

So how does this apply to the global economy today? Simple, it is all about the "Demand Information Bank", and mobility is ushering in a new, unprecedented era where real-time communications with consumers at the point-of-purchase will allow manufacturers to interact with and influence buying decisions in totally new ways. Companies that can *capture* a meaningful amount of demand data in real-time in any market and *act* on it will be able to use that information to optimize their operations and profit at the expense of the other participants in the supply chain. For the winners, this will mean significantly higher profits on the same set of assets. For the losers, it will mean an increasingly tenuous market position with many of the most famous names in the world simply being relegated to irrelevance or worse. The old adage that information is power is about to be turbo charged and in its wake will be a reshuffling of the economic order in nearly every industry.

Chapter VI: The Case of the Nervous Cow from Kansas

"Eat Mor Chikin"® – The Chick-fil-A® Cows

At the height of the Internet mania that swept the world economy in the late 1990s, there was a popular little saying that graced many presentations of the day: "When a New Yorker orders a hamburger, a cow in Kansas gets nervous."[17] It was a graphic and somewhat humorous (although perhaps not so funny to animal rights activists) way of pointing out that the Internet was extending supply chains across corporate boundaries and intensively integrating business operations. Sell a hamburger, kill a

---

[17] Despite my best efforts I cannot locate the originator of this quote.

cow. Sell a computer, burn a mother board. Sell something, do something. The perfectly integrated supply chain of the global economy was creating greater and greater efficiencies between companies.

In a very literal and physical way it marked the point at which some people began to recognize that everything behaves just like Enron's gas pipelines – gas goes in, gas goes out, and information about both is critical. One of the main ideas propounded by The Fourth Shock is that whoever can figure out a sustainable informational advantage about the relative balance of supply and demand can make money across the entire spectrum of the value chain, not just their own relatively small piece of it. Furthermore, the world has gotten pretty darn good at managing the information in the supply-side of the equation, but the demand-side is where the action will be in the coming years. The all important first step is to emulate Enron and find that informational choke point where supply meets demand.

In the previous chapter, we saw how Enron had a knack for looking at industry supply chains in a slightly different way than the rest of the world. Essentially, they viewed an industry as a means of moving demand information from the consumer to the supplier, and vice versa, and then looked to pick off strategic points in that flow in order to capture real-time demand trends ahead of the other participants in the market. They then combined that information with world class trading technologies and strategies to extract economic profits from all parts of the supply chain. Nice work if you can get it; and it seemed to work in the gas and electricity markets, but how could you possibly apply that strategy in other industries, such as consumer packaged goods or fast food? These industries are not really commodity based businesses in the traditional sense of the word, and they are not undergoing the traumatic effects of government deregulation.

However, what they all have in common is exactly what the Fourth Shock embodies, which is the shift from a supply-centric view of the world to one that uses new technologies to capture and benefit from real-time demand data. It states that the single most important thing in the world for businesses is the ability to aggregate a meaningful amount of demand data before everyone else in the supply chain and to use that information to radically increase profits on an existing set of assets. In economic terms it argues that the marginal utility of additional assets is directly related to the amount in which such assets meaningfully increase an organization's ability to understand overall market demand. At some point more pipelines, more outlets, more production can become wasted energy and resources. The only thing that truly matters to any for-profit operation is timely, actionable insights on demand. Everything else is superfluous.

In order to make the point, let's apply the lessons of Enron to one of the most famous and recognizable brands in the world – McDonald's. I could choose just about any company, but the significant market share McDonald's enjoys will drive home the example. It is also somewhat directly related to that nervous cow referred to in this chapter's title.

McDonald's extensive network of restaurants and franchisees sits at an interesting intersection of supply and demand data in the fast food industry. As the world's largest hamburger fast food chain, the company serves around 58 million customers daily and boasts over 31,000 restaurants in 118 countries. It is also arguably the single most recognizable brand in the world.

McDonald's isn't just big, it is also impressively efficient. The restaurant industry in the United States consists of approximately 575,000 restaurants, and in 2008 that industry generated around $370 billion in annual sales. McDonald's restaurants comprised 2.4% of the total number but its $23,522,400,000 in revenue represents approximately 8% of the industry's total sales. The company also currently employs more than 1.5 million people with some estimates stating that about one in eight of all Americans have worked for McDonald's at some point in their lives.[18]

Given their flagship product and their policy of not actually producing anything that they serve, it is easy to see why McDonald's is the number one buyer of beef in the country. It is also the number one buyer of pork, potatoes,

---

[18] In his research for the book Fast Food Nation, author Eric Scholsser found that 1 in 8 Americans have worked for McDonald's at some point in their lives. Subsequent news reports by Fox News have placed the number at one in ten.

and oddly enough, apples. As a testament to their marketing prowess, McDonald's is also the largest private operator of playgrounds in the United States.[19]

Like many other great institutions, McDonald's has an interesting history. The company got its start as a BBQ drive-in opened in 1940 by two brothers, Dick and Mac McDonald, in San Bernardino, California. It had a large menu, but hamburgers seemed to far outsell the other items. After several years of noticing this demand data trend, the brothers decided to make the hamburger the focus of their business. In 1948 they closed their restaurant for a few months to implement an assembly line system for quicker production of their hamburgers. It was called the "Speedee Service System." Upon reopening, their hamburgers sold more than ever, and due to their cheap price – 15¢ at the time – and the speed of the service, the restaurant's reputation spread quickly by word of mouth.

Following on the heels of their initial success, the brothers opened their first few franchises in 1953. A year later a milkshake mixer salesman named Ray Kroc went on a sales call to the brothers' restaurant and was so impressed with its popularity that he decided to change his profession. Kroc persuaded the McDonald brothers to allow him to

---

[19] As the father of three young kids I can verify that my wife and I cannot come within ½ a mile of a McDonald's without our kids going into some sort of McDonald's induced seizure that causes them to uncontrollably scream "Donald's!" over and over again.

aggressively extend their franchise outside of their main base of California, and in 1955 he opened a new McDonald's in Des Plaines, IL. From that point forward, Kroc fanatically pushed the McDonald's brand and by 1959 he had helped the company open its 100th restaurant.

In 1961, Kroc convinced the McDonald brothers to sell the business rights for their operation to him for $2.7 million, which was not an insignificant amount at the time. Not long after that, his relationship with the brothers rapidly deteriorated. The brothers claim they made a verbal agreement with Kroc that entitled them to a 1% royalty on gross sales going forward. During the negotiations Kroc had demanded the property rights of the original location be turned over to him at the close of the deal. The brothers refused citing their desire to give the real estate and rights over to the founding employees of the location. At the deal closing table, Kroc still seethed at the idea of not getting the original location, so after the deal was done, he refused to honor the royalty agreement. If that handshake agreement still stood today, the families of the McDonald's would be collecting over $150 million every year.

But Kroc wasn't satisfied with simply pulling the royalty deal. In their zeal to retain the rights to the original McDonald's location, the McDonald brothers failed to negotiate the right to remain a McDonald's franchisee. Kroc promptly revoked those rights and the brothers were forced to change the name of their cherished location to the "The Big M". Kroc then proceeded to open a McDonald's franchise a block away and subsequently put them out of business.

By 1968, the company had opened its 1,000th restaurant. In only 13 years, Kroc had taken McDonald's from less than 10 restaurants to 1,000. The company continued to grow aggressively over the decades, and by 1995 it had reached a point in the eyes of some of their franchisees that they had actually expanded too much. There were so many McDonald's restaurants in the country that it had begun to breed competition amongst them. Although the situation never got to the point where mass closings were in order, the corporate headquarters now does extensive research before it flippantly grants franchise permission.

As this brief history shows, McDonald's has reached the point of market saturation and has to find new ways to make more money from its existing network of franchisees. One way to do this would be to invert its business model to leverage the information in its distribution network to create new profit opportunities. So what information does McDonald's have that no one else in the world has and cannot have? With their tremendous scale, they have the unique ability to roll up demand data on a significant percentage of global demand for a number of commodities. Like Enron, they don't need to have all the demand data, just more than anyone else. In the supply chain that starts with justifiably paranoid cows and apparently clueless potatoes and ends with sated diners, McDonald's exist at the choke point for a significant amount of demand data.

The Fourth Shock

Of course, as the story of Ray Kroc's hard-nosed business practices can attest, McDonald's didn't become one of the largest restaurant companies in the world by sitting around twiddling their thumbs. In an industry that is notoriously unforgiving to start ups and operates on razor thin margins, McDonald's boasts some of the most sophisticated supply chain management systems in the world. Every day the company sources local meats, produce, milk and dairy products around the world to insure the freshest ingredients are used to uphold corporate quality standards. It is truly a modern marvel of logistics, marketing, and supply chain and brand management.

Every cash register in every McDonald's is the open end of a pipeline that captures point-of-sale data through the exchange of food for money. The company uses that information in conjunction with other traditional sources of demand information to optimize purchasing decisions, much as Enron's competitors used supply and demand data and trading to hedge against production risk. But what if McDonald's started its own version of Enron Capital & Trade? "McTrade" would be in the enviable position of being able to roll up demand data globally for all the beef sold in the company's far flung operations and use that information to gauge global demand trends for beef long before (relatively speaking) most of the other participants in the supply chain knew what was going on. The ability to generate, capture and analyze unique real-time information in the beef markets would constitute the same type of sustainable advantage Enron enjoyed in the natural gas market.

Let's assume McTrade actually exists and its mandate is to enhance the profitability of McDonald's by using the unique demand data available to the company to leverage the supply chain. As supply and demand trends became apparent, McTrade would use sophisticated trading technologies and strategies to generate profits, essentially from the same set of assets the company already owns. These added profits would then be used to more aggressively market McDonald's products, which in turn would ideally create more unique demand data, which in turn would enhance the company's trading positions, on and on ad infinitum. Like Enron's Gas Bank, a company like McDonald's that finds itself at the nexus of a meaningful amount of supply and demand data in any market can implement an inversion of the business model that has the potential to create a virtuous feedback cycle.

One of the fundamental arguments of the Fourth Shock is that the optimal price of a good is not solely tied to marginal cost of production but rather it is the marginal cost of production minus any aggregate informational advantage derived from the transaction. In many cases, it may be better to price a good lower than "normal" in order to aggregate a meaningful amount of demand data if the organization accumulating the demand data can act on it to profit from the rest of the supply chain. This is a fairly radical idea, but one that will become a key competitive weapon in many industries as the Fourth Shock takes hold across the economy.[20]

Of course, very few companies are fortunate enough to sit at the pinnacle of their industries and have the ability to aggregate demand data from so many points across the globe. Interestingly, history shows us that companies that are in this position are often the most reluctant to embrace radical new business models and paradigms.[21] Would McDonald's actually risk inverting their entire world view to squeeze out additional profits from its existing asset base?[22] Unlikely.

The unprecedented availability of increasing amounts of real-time and near real-time demand data is tantamount to a

---

[20] One obvious risk in this approach is the possibility of focusing too much on the generation and capture of unique demand information at the expense of product quality. However, any company that did this would ultimately see a decrease in the relative amount of proprietary demand information available. Conversely, if a company's combination of product quality and competitive pricing increases its overall percentage of proprietary demand information, the company would be able to even more aggressively press its advantage over competitors and the supply chain.

[21] *The Innovator's Dilemma* by Clayton M. Christensen does a great job of explaining this phenomenon.

[22] Even if McDonald's never implements a McTrade-type addition to its corporate profit mix, at the very least the company could sell its real-time demand data or partner with third parties who do make a living in the commodities markets.

fundamental shock to the business environment, every bit as disruptive as the phenomena of punctuated equilibrium discussed earlier. However, incumbents in every market will be limited by their past successes and will focus on continuing to create and deploy innovations that extend existing systems and business processes. For example, railroad companies in the 1800s were the wealthiest most sophisticated corporations in the world who hired simply the best and brightest minds of the day, yet not one of them made the transition to the automobile industry when consumer preferences shifted.

This is why the Fourth Shock is hardly limited to market leaders. Although they are in the best position to take advantage of this new way of focusing on and profiting from demand data rather than sticking to the reactive nature of supply chain data, markets leaders are the least likely to do so because "you don't fix what ain't broken." This opens the field up to every other company in the world and allows them to use the first principle of the Fourth Shock to increasingly gain market share and outperform the likes of McDonald's, just as the HNG/InterNorth upstart did in the gas industry in the 1980s and 1990s. In the hands of a smart, committed corporation, even small demand data advantages at various points throughout the supply chain can have huge implications for growth and profitability over the long term.[23]

---

[23] A great resource for understanding this concept can be found once again in the realm of evolutionary biology. In

The Fourth Shock

McTrade and its ilk may represent an ambitious idea that lies outside of the comfort zone of many management teams and shareholders, especially those that have been most successful with the supply-chain centric view of the world. The idea that a company's primary purpose lies in its ability to capture real-time demand data and use it effectively to gain sustainable competitive advantage is simply not how most of the world looks at data up to this point. But as a wise old Wall Street saying goes, "past performance is not necessarily indicative of future performance." The Fourth Shock's first rule of using unique demand data to invert the business model is arguably a strategy of choice, at least to this point in the economic development of most of the global economy. A company can *opt* to implement an inversion strategy of capturing demand data and using significant trading operations based on that data to enhance profitability, but it won't be *forced* to do so until one of its competitors does it successfully. However, as we will soon see there is an alternative method of using demand data that has proven to be equally effective

---

particular, Richard Dawkins fascinating book The Blind Watchmaker does a wonderful job of explaining how small information advantages (to use my terms) can have unbelievable long term effects. Also, for a good view of the concentration of force and its effectiveness across a broad front, I point the reader to Mao Tse Tung's On Protracted War. In it Mao argues that although his forces are outnumbered overall, he can concentrate his forces at any given point and gain numerical superiority at that point, provided he is the one on the initiative.

at generating above market rates of profitability and building significant barriers to entry.

Chapter VII: The Three E's on the Road to Demand Data Dominance

"Even if you're on the right track, you'll get run over if you just sit there."
- Will Rogers

If Wal-Mart were a country and its revenue were equivalent to Gross Domestic Product it would rank as the 27the largest economy in the world. In 2008 it was the biggest company in the world with revenue topping $400 billion and employees totaling over 2,000,000 people globally. Admittedly comparing revenue to GDP is not really an apples-to-apples comparison, but it's a reasonable approximation for our purposes. The company's 2008 revenue would place it just ahead of Greece on a ranking of countries by GDP and ahead of countries such as Denmark,

Argentina and Ireland. Think about that for a second. The two million employees of Wal-Mart generate more economic value that the 41 million people living in Argentina. Again, this isn't a perfect comparison, but it is insightful.

Every week over 100 million customers pass in and out of Wal-Mart's doors – the approximate equivalent of a third of the population of the United States. Wal-Mart's biggest direct competitor in the general merchandising world is Target Corp. No slouch in its own right, Target generated $63 billion in revenue in 2008, or about 1/6th that of Wal-Mart.

Even more astonishing than the amount of revenue Wal-Mart generates annually is the rate they have been able to consistently increase revenue over the last 20 years. In 1988, Wal-Mart's revenue was "only" $20.6 billion. The same year the GDP of France was a little over $1 trillion. By the end of the 2008 fiscal year, Wal-Mart's revenue had soared to $401 billion while France's GDP had reached $2.09 trillion. Again, not a perfect comparison, but as an interesting and amusing fact, if both Wal-Mart and France maintained their average growth rates over the past 20 years into the future, by the year 2016 Wal-Mart's revenue would exceed the GDP of the entire nation of France.

Although the comparisons to France are interesting and in my opinion somewhat humorous, a more meaningful and insightful comparison is the relative performance of Wal-Mart with long time dominant retailers Sears Roebuck &

The Fourth Shock

Co. and Kmart (now joined together as Sears Holdings Corporation after their merger in 2005).

Sears was started all the way back in 1893 when Richard Warren Sears, who had started a catalogue to sell watches, met Alvah C. Roebuck and the two formed a business called Sears, Roebuck and Co. Throughout the first quarter of the 20th century, the catalogue grew to well over 500 pages and included items as varied as sewing machines, dolls, stoves, bicycles and groceries.

The first Sears retail store opened its doors in Chicago in 1925 and during the latter half of the 1920s others soon followed. Sears experienced significant growth during the ensuing years and by 1945 the company's annual sales surpassed the $1 billion mark. From the 1940s to the 1970s, Sears reveled in its position as the dominant retailer in the United States – maybe a bit too much.

Similar to Sears, Kmart's history dates all the way back to the 19th century. In 1899, Sebastian Spering Kresge took over a chain of 5¢ & 10¢ stores he had started with a business partner after their relationship soured. He formed the S.S. Kresge Company and built it to more than 85 stores and $10 million in sales by 1912. The company was so successful that it went public in 1918. By 1929 the company boasted nearly six hundred stores generating over $156 million in sales per year.

In 1962, Kresge decided to open a new kind of retail store that would be much larger than anything the company had done previously. Located in Garden City, MI, the new store was named Kmart and before the year was over seventeen more of them would debut all around the country. In 1966, Kmart's sales topped $1 billion for the first time. During the 1970s Kmart put quite a few of its rival retailers out of business in the local markets it entered, and with Kmart now accounting for 95% of the sales of all the S.S. Kresge Company's holdings, the company was reincorporated as the Kmart Corporation.

Kmart ended the 1980 fiscal year with a company record $14.2 billion in sales. The rest of the decade would not be as kind to Kmart as the company came to be seen by the public as outdated. Many stores had become somewhat rundown and the company seemed to be more focused on its rivalry with Sears than on its customers. Kmart struggled to regain momentum, renovating some stores and trying various short term changes, but these efforts were half-hearted. While Wal-Mart was focused on its core business and busy embracing its supply chain partners, Kmart's management team was busy trying to integrate a number of distracting acquisitions such as Waldenbooks and The Sports Authority. By 1990, Wal-Mart surpassed Kmart in annual sales.

During the 1980s and 1990s, Sears and Kmart embraced in a myopic and fatally symbiotic dance of one-upmanship while Wal-Mart steadily implemented the foundation it would need to dominate the industry by focusing on understanding consumer behavior through the capture of demand data.

The year 1979 marked the first time Wal-Mart's annual sales surpassed $1 billion, with a figure of $1.2 billion.

This was a full 34 years after Sears hit that impressive mark and 14 years after Kmart. The annual sales figure for Sears in the 1980 fiscal year was approximately $17.5 billion and as stated earlier Kmart weighed in at $14.2 billion. Despite the huge advantage in market share enjoyed by the market leaders, Wal-Mart methodically dismantled both of them in the coming years.

By 2005, the competitive situation with Wal-Mart had become so dire for Sears and Kmart that the two long time rivals were forced to merge in a desperate attempt to stay relevant and competitive. Even with the merger, the new Sears Holding Corporation pales in comparison to Wal-Mart. In 2008 Wal-Mart posted sales of over $400 billion while the tag-team combination of Sears and Kmart mustered $50 billion.

How is it possible that a general store from small-town Arkansas evolved into a corporation that absolutely crushed the longtime industry leaders and whose wealth-generating capacity now rivals that of major European nations? The answer lies in two key factors.

The first is the company's fanatical pursuit of low prices. To paraphrase political advisor James Carville's famous phrase, "It's the prices stupid." While Sears and Kmart were busy buying other companies and expanding their business empires into areas that did not add value to their core customer, Wal-Mart remained focused on getting the lowest prices for their shoppers. And the main way they did this was by the second key factor – the innovative use of demand data.

The Fourth Shock

As we shall soon see, Wal-Mart's unmatched understanding and use of demand data fueled their relentless growth while simultaneously providing them with an avenue to consistently offer the lowest prices to their shoppers. This virtuous cycle of increasing amounts of demand data driving lower prices, and lower prices driving increasing amounts of demand data, is the key to Wal-Mart's dominance of the retail industry.

Unlike Enron, Wal-Mart doesn't use demand data to trade on information advantages, but rather captures and analyzes demand information and shares its insights with its partners in the supply chain to create a win-win-win situation for themselves, the supplier and the consumer.

In the late 1940s, Sam Walton ran a franchise of a retail chain called Ben Franklin in Newport, Arkansas. While fairly successful, lease renewal complications ended up pushing him to move to another town, Bentonville, Arkansas, where he ended up buying a general store from a man named Luther Harrison in 1950. He named this store "Walton's 5 & 10." Once established in Bentonville, Walton figured out an uncommon means to profit. Like any other retailer, he scoured the market always searching for deals from suppliers, but unlike the competition, when he got a deal he would pass the discount along to the customer. And what happened? He got more customers making more purchases coming through his doors. Walton had figured out one of the earliest aspects of what has made Wal-Mart into what it is today. He could make more by marking up his products less than his competitors and earning his profit on volume of sales rather than price mark up. Price cutting was the first innovation that led to Wal-Mart becoming essentially the positive feedback cycle of a retailer that it is today. The lower he put his prices, the more customers would flock to his store. This in turn meant that as more customers flocked to his store, he could present suppliers with greater sales volumes, which in turn enticed the supplier to give Walton even better prices. This led to more customers…and well, here we go again.

The first actual Wal-Mart opened in Rogers, Arkansas, in 1962. Walton's cost cutting continued to bring in more and more customers, and the company expanded. Growth was massive for Wal-Mart throughout the '70s, and when the decade closed the retail chain could boast 276 stores in 11 states, 21,000 associates, and $1.2 billion in sales generated.

If down to the bone cost cutting was what put Wal-Mart on the national map, an innovation that took place within the company in the 1980s would place it prominently on the storyline of history. In addition to his obsessions with low prices and high volume sales, Sam Walton was seriously committed to developing a strong culture across the company and he was borderline compulsive about studying detailed sales data on a daily basis.

Developing a strong culture may be somewhat of an understatement. A more accurate description would be Walton pushed a culture that bordered on the cultish. Employees would take oaths of customer service that ended with "so help me Sam." Walton was a huge stickler for enforcing a policy of his employees looking any customers within their proximity directly in the eye and offering help. Personal contact was a must. That's why, for the first few decades of Wal-Mart's existence, he would travel to each store personally to meet staff and customers in order to get a first person view of how the store was running.

By the '80s, Wal-Mart had expanded to the point where visiting each store one by one was becoming no longer feasible. This really annoyed Walton, so much so that it caused him to do something that was very out of character. The man famous for frugality and thrift decided to throw $24 million into an investment that involved outer space. It was a satellite system that would link each store, and allow the owner to beam his pep talks to employees all around the country any time he desired.

Although connectivity to his stores was a major factor, there was a second selling point that was just as important to Walton, and that was data. *Fortune* magazine later claimed "Walton couldn't get enough of it, and the company's jammed telephone lines couldn't handle it."[24] With the installation of this new satellite system, Wal-Mart could track data in all of their stores. In addition, Walton could continue to hold staff meetings, as he so loved to do on his visits, with all the stores across the country simultaneously. The satellite system was up and running by 1987 and almost immediately began to impact the

---

[24] Jerry Useem, "20 That Made History," *Fortune*, June 27, 2005

company's growth. The ability to capture and analyze demand data on an almost real-time basis allowed Wal-Mart to rapidly spot trends and react to them. As *Fortune* magazine put it when looking back on this late '80s innovation, "In 1985, two years before the completion of the system, Wal-Mart's sales were $8.4 billion. Ten years later, they were $93.6 billion. Ten years after that, they had left the atmosphere altogether: $288 billion, a number without historical precedent."[25]

Not unlike Enron's use of demand data in their pipelines and power plants, Wal-Mart led the retailing world in recognizing the value of real-time demand data. The company's first-of-its-kind data gathering system allowed it to leapfrog competitors and scale to unprecedented heights by capturing demand data and using it wisely. If you think about it, Wal-Mart isn't terribly dissimilar to a pipeline, albeit a fairly complex one. Wal-Mart doesn't produce anything, but it is simply a conduit for linking supply and demand – goods go in one side and out the other. What they excel at is using the real-time demand data flowing from their stores to radically increase profitability. Enron did the same thing and then used that information to make extraordinary profits in the commodities markets. Wal-Mart, on the other hand, uses this information to not only increase its own profitability, but the profitability of all the participants in the supply chain.

---

[25] Useem, "20 That Made History"

The Fourth Shock

This is the first of the three "E's" noted in the title of this chapter - *Embrace*. In 1991, Wal-Mart took the unprecedented step of allowing its suppliers to benefit from the data flowing from its satellite system. In other words, rather than see their suppliers as adversaries to be disaggregated and marginalized, Wal-Mart embraced them as a virtual extension of their own business. Dubbed Retail Link, Wal-Mart's proprietary data gathering system records the sale of every item in every Wal-Mart for every hour of the day. It can provide formatted reports to a supplier about anomalies in product performance in certain regions, giving the supplier the information needed to figure out how to remedy the problem. When shipments of new products go out to Wal-Mart stores, Retail Link can even inform the supplier as to which stores have the product on shelves, which have the product in the storage room, and which stores have not yet received shipments. Using this information a supplier can better understand sales trends in various areas and respond appropriately.

Wal-Mart's Retail Link is a very tangible demonstration of the company's commitment to embracing its supply chain and working together for mutual benefit. From early on Wal-Mart seemed to view their relationship with their suppliers as a synergy. Often big merchandisers such as Sears, the quintessential American merchandiser, treated that same relationship as more one-sided, as though suppliers would be lost without such a strongly branded retailer in their corner. But Wal-Mart embraces their suppliers, knowing that the highest rate of success will come through cooperation, and that often the better a supplier does the better Wal-Mart will do.

In 2005, an article in *Retailing Today* quoted Wal-Mart's vice president of merchandising systems Dan Phillips as saying, "Use Retail Link and it will grow your business at Wal-Mart. Just get in there, understand how to use it and explore its capabilities and it will help a supplier grow their business at Wal-Mart. Then use it to leverage your business at Wal-Mart."[26] The very nature of Retail Link is to perform the second E – *Empower*. Wal-Mart empowers their suppliers by giving them the demand information they need to better understand what is going on in its stores. Wal-Mart's desire in doing so is to make its entire supply chain more efficient so that the suppliers can lower their costs to Wal-Mart and Wal-Mart can in turn offer lower prices to its customers. Retail Link is the key component in the process.

The success of this approach has not gone unnoticed by other retailers. Accordingly, many companies have begun to emulate Wal-Mart and its Retail Link system, but it still stands as the most successful demand data gathering and distribution system by a singular company today. They literally have an informational advantage in informational advantages.

In embracing their supply chain by allowing them into the Wal-Mart sales process and empowering the supply

---

[26] Mike Troy, "Refining Retail Link," *DSN Retailing Today*, September 12, 2005

chain by offering unprecedented access to the myriad data that would normally only be for the eyes of the merchandiser itself, Wal-Mart is able to demand the lowest price from their suppliers. But the payback for the suppliers who support these efforts is a continual access to millions and millions of shoppers every day. In the parlance of the E's of demand data dominance the third E occurs when participants in the value chain assist each other in generating greater overall sales and is known as *Extend*.

The whole point of Wal-Mart's empowering of their supply chain with massive amounts of demand data is so that the product sales of the supplier can be extended. Wal-Mart has amassed the largest customer base in the retail industry by focusing on and enabling the lowest possible prices, and this in turn drives increasing amounts of customers. Wal-Mart's offer to producers: use our data management system to figure out the most efficient way to sell your product, cut your costs on the production and distribution end, cut your prices to us, we will cut costs to customers, and thereby we will aggregate an even greater number of customers to buy even more of your product. And the number of customers Wal-Mart has aggregated is what makes suppliers desire to get into the game and perform better in the first place. It is a positive feedback cycle that has generated revenue that rivals the GDP of nations.

It isn't as though it's just some carefree, supplier-centered system. Wal-Mart wants to extend its suppliers' success to their own ends, of course, and the shelves of its distribution centers are not friendly to those products that don't flourish. It is a clear case of starving the weak to feed the strong. Wal-Mart wants its suppliers' products to sell well, but if they don't, the shelf space is needed and quickly appropriated for other vendors with better selling goods.

One of the most important factors in Wal-Mart's data gathering is the expanse of their choke points. Wal-Mart captures data every minute of the day from consumers in more than 8,000 stores around the world. They were the first to collect demand data and distribute it across the supply chain so their suppliers could benefit from it as well. As other competitors emulate this approach, Wal-Mart will still have an advantage because their network of data collection points is larger, and their unmatched historical data gives them the ability to get better results through long-term trend analysis. While other companies can implement Retail Link-like systems, no one else has a customer base or a data pool aggregated to the same level as Wal-Mart.

Wal-Mart is essentially Enron's pipeline – a way of gathering demand data and using that data to more effectively connect supply and demand, all the while profiting from the effort. What does Wal-Mart produce? Nothing. Everything they sell is brought in from suppliers. But with a single-minded focus on one key value – lowest prices possible – they have found ways to embrace, empower and extend their supply chain to become one of the largest and most successful companies in the history of the world.

Chapter VIII: Demand Data as a Tool for Dominating the Supply Chain

"Resistance is futile. Your life as it has been is over. From this time forward, you will service us...You will be assimilated."

- Locutus of Borg

The May 5, 1996 cover of Boardwatch magazine featured a now famous image of Billgatus of Borg (a.k.a Bill Gates). The unflattering image pictured Gates wearing headgear of the dreaded Borg from the Star Trek series with a necklace of corporate logos of all the companies Microsoft had destroyed in its climb to market dominance. Dead center in the targeting eyepiece of the headgear can be seen the Netscape logo. The text surrounding the image stated simply, "Resistance is futile, you will be assimilated." At the time Microsoft and Netscape were locked in a bitter struggle for market dominance of the newly minted web browser market, and the unsubtle implication of the cover was that it was only a matter of time before Netscape would be destroyed. Unfortunately for Netscape, it was eerily accurate.

This image of a dreaded, inexorable force juxtaposes oddly with the Microsoft of the early 1980s. At that time, Microsoft was seen by most software developers as a powerful force of good, and the company was dismissed by industry heavy weights as at best an insignificant necessity. Once again, it was the ability of the company to acquire an informational advantage about consumer demand that transformed it into a veritable Borg of the global economy.

It is interesting to note that Microsoft and Wal-Mart began executing on the three E's of demand data dominance at almost the same time. It is arguable that Microsoft was the better of the two at using its advantageous position in capturing demand data to embrace, empower and extend the value of its partners across the value chain and create a win-win-win for itself, its partners and PC consumers. Microsoft was so good at it in fact, they added a fourth E – exterminate – that earned it Borg status in the eyes of many.

Obviously Microsoft wasn't simply plunked down on earth with access to an information advantage in the software industry. It had to earn it. As we discussed in chapter three, DOS came about through some smart moves on the part of Microsoft and a little luck. Getting paired up with IBM and establishing a standard allowed Microsoft to grow very rapidly. We also hinted to the fact that, like Wal-Mart, Microsoft performed some brilliant implementation of the three E's – embrace, empower, extend. Here is how they did it.

As DOS entered the enterprise software fray in the early 1980s, Microsoft took a far more aggressive approach than any other operating systems competitors to embrace the entire supply chain. Unlike Apple, who took an approach to software developers and hardware manufacturers that bordered on the adversarial, Microsoft quickly discerned that an operating system is only as valuable as the software running on it. In this they closely resembled Wal-Mart's approach we discussed in the previous chapter wherein a retail store is only as valuable as the retail products that are in it. Further extending its similarities to Wal-Mart, Microsoft also recognized that the low price, high volume, high value provider would have a distinct advantage in the operating system marketplace. This combination of embracing their partners and focusing on being low-cost and high-volume drove the beginnings of a virtuous cycle.[27]

In Microsoft's case embracing the supply chain meant that their system was open and easily accessible for

---

[27] "DOS was one of first really affordable operating systems. Digital Research wanted $495 for CP/M-86. IBM sold PC-DOS was [sic] $40 and many software developers found it easier to port existing CP/M software to DOS than to the new version of CP/M. Since IBM's $39.95 DOS was far cheaper than anyone else's alternative everyone bought DOS." - Dr. Nokolai Bezroukov: The Orthodox File Manager Paradigm

software developers. The company actively and relentlessly pursued software developers of all kinds to write software for DOS. They made it clear that the ultimate value of DOS was not in the operating system per se, but rather the value-added software running on it.

If you had heard Bill Gates speaking in the early '80s, he would have spent the majority of any presentation describing how the value of Microsoft was driven by its partners not by Microsoft itself. Time after time he harped on these innovative software developers that were creating thousands of different kinds of software that could run on Microsoft's product. By contrast, Apple mirrored Sears with its insistence on controlling every aspect of the value chain and the technology "stack" – hardware, operating system and software applications. This attitude meant that small software developers in particular could not afford to meet Apple's demanding standards and fees, so they opted for the less powerful and eloquent, but cheaper and more open DOS. Of course, in these early days software, many of the most creative and innovative software was being developed in garages and dorm rooms across the country. They overwhelmingly embraced DOS as their system of choice, which meant that DOS users were the main beneficiaries of their efforts.

I cannot overstate the impact of two critical mistakes Apple made early on. Although controlling the whole stack comes with greater efficiencies in system performance, it limits the ability of outsiders to add value to the overall consumer value proposition. In a period of relative stability where markets are clearly defined and changes are more incremental in nature, this holistic approach may work, and in some instances could even be more efficient, but in a period of rapid change and massive uncertainty, an approach that rewards risk taking, or to use the biological example from Chapter One, mutations, has a distinct advantage. At the dawn of PC software programming the field "was quite open for anybody with talent to make his/her mark: it was era of re-invention of old concepts on a new level and creation of new one, kind of programming gold rush."[28]

The second critical error in Apple's approach was in pricing its products too high. Because of the incredible rate of change in the market, consumers were wary of buying a computer for fear it would be obsolete by the time they learned how to use it. A high price posed a huge problem for users as they would see their investment plummet in very short order, so they were inclined to either wait for a price drop or buy a cheaper machine.

But because Apple controlled all aspects of the stack, their customers could not benefit from real competition that would have driven prices lower across every component. In economic terms Apple had "pricing power," which investors absolutely love. However, in this case it was counter-productive to Apple's long term dominance of the operating system and subsequently the software market.

---

[28] Dr. Nokolai Bezroukov: The Orthodox File Manager Paradigm

The Fourth Shock

Both of these strategic errors led to Apple's overall superior system losing out to the far inferior DOS. In the parlance of the Fourth Shock, Apple's strategy retarded the network effects of the three E's while Microsoft embraced them.

Microsoft's strategy was to open the system up – to get as many partners as possible. If you as a user purchased a computer because you wanted to run a spreadsheet application, Microsoft DOS users could select from numerous competing products whereas in Apple your choices were much more limited. Because they embraced the entire supply chain, Microsoft didn't care which spreadsheet you ultimately used, as long as it ran in DOS. Gates and company were very shrewd at selling the value of embracing partners to both software developers and PC consumers.

By doing so they established the foundation for a very successful positive feedback loop. Microsoft opened up the market, partnered with many developers of different kinds of software, and offered numerous valuable options to their customers. That was their model, and it was a steady, consistent message. Furthermore, in an oddity from today's point of view, at the time it was Apple that was seen as competing with their partners whereas Microsoft was viewed by the software developer community as fairly hands off and non-threatening.

Microsoft did more than merely embrace the supply chain and offer a low price for DOS that started to create a mass market. In order to accelerate that mass market's growth and continue to add value for DOS users, the company took great pains to empower its partners to be more successful. As mentioned earlier, many of the software development companies of the early '80s were bootstrap outfits consisting of mostly kids and hobbyists. It was people in their garages and dorm rooms after work or school. There were certainly some business applications being written by larger companies, but by and large software was being written by amateurs who wanted to play computer games or simply experiment. On the grand scale computers were fairly new to the everyday person and thus incredibly interesting to many. Microsoft recognized that and empowered them in three primary ways.

The first way they empowered these developers was by selling them DOS at a very reasonable price, thus creating a critical mass of users for the software market. If you could write some decent software, Microsoft, as Gates was always ready to point out, had a relatively large installed base of users. Therefore, by writing software for DOS a software developer could reach an ever increasing amount of potential customers.

Secondly, Microsoft aggressively supported software developers' efforts by releasing a series of "software development toolkits", or SDKs. The company consistently released updates and tools designed to make writing software for DOS easier and more efficient. For example, some of these SDKs were designed to help a developer test the code in various environments or run quality control. Due to the nature of their "embrace" strategy and the large software development community it spawned, it was imperative that Microsoft lead in these types of efforts. A positive side effect was that these developers pushed the limits of Microsoft's own code and helped quickly improve the overall quality of DOS – all-in-all a very smart and successful strategy.

To further enhance the value of their empowerment strategy, Microsoft often gave these SDKs away for free or for very little costs. All of this combined to create a compelling set of incentives and benefits to software developers, resulting in a significant payoff. By 1984, Microsoft could boast that DOS had 10 times the number of software titles than its nearest rival. These actions were also not far afield from that of Wal-Mart offering the Retail Link data to retailers, so that they would perform better on the shelves. It's empowerment. By embracing and empowering their supply chain, Microsoft created tremendous value for its own operating system and the end users who purchased it.

The next step in Microsoft's march towards dominating the software industry came with its concerted efforts to extend the value of its partners' products across the installed base of DOS – the third E. Today, software companies have grown and can often hire the necessary sales and marketing expertise to effectively distribute their product. However, in the early 1980s this was not usually the case. Frankly, most software developers at the time were atrocious at selling it.

The Fourth Shock

If you have ever had the chance to hang out with hardcore software developers, the first thing that might impress you is their formidable skills in mathematics that allow them to make computers do some amazing things. On the other hand, you may determine that many or even most of them are not what you might call classical salesmen. This stereotype has changed significantly over the decades, but the early 1980s was where the stereotype first evolved.

At that time the single most daunting problem for software developers was figuring out a way to sell their software. Most had no idea where to even begin that process, and even those who figured it out simply weren't comfortable doing it. Microsoft's genius, very similar to Wal-Mart's genius and interestingly occurring at almost the exact same time, was to help the supply chain sell more software. Who else was going to offer that? Sears tried to disaggregate their suppliers. Apple did the same thing. Both were busy trying to disaggregate their suppliers so they could take all of the profit.

Microsoft stepped into the role of chief sales and marketing officer for hundreds of software companies and helped them sell their software at no additional cost. So not only did they embrace the supply chain to get everyone writing software for DOS, and not only did they empower the supply chain with SDKs and a low price point, but they actually helped their partners sell more software.

For example, if you had heard Bill Gates give a presentation in 1985, you would have heard him wax eloquent about the fact that the value of DOS was truly driven by its partners across the supply chain. One such partner that may have warranted a mention would have been XTREE and their innovative file management utility for DOS. Today, a computer user who wants to find a stored file can go the file management utility and see a visible representation of all the computer's files. It's all visual and fairly easy to navigate. But in the early days of the PC and DOS it was nowhere near as convenient. First of all the interface was not graphical; it was navigated by what is called a command prompt. A user was required to type in a long list of symbols and commands in order to get a computer to do something. The following set of commands would have told a DOS computer in 1983 to present on screen the list of all the subdirectories on your hard drive.

C:> DIR *.* /S /P

This was just one of hundreds of arcane bits of knowledge required to interface with computers of the day. The above example, C:> was known as the command prompt. The "DIR" was the command for listing out a directory, and "*.*" was the command to display files of all types. "/S" meant to also include subdirectories in the display, and "/P" told the computer to list the results by page so the information didn't just scroll off the bottom of the screen. That was the process to display your subdirectories. How many average computer users today would be able to deal with computing every day if such a simple task still required that kind of knowledge and work?

In the mid-80s a piece of software was created called XTree[29]. A typical Microsoft moment of the day would have seen Bill Gates get up on stage at a computer convention of some sort and claim that the reason you should buy DOS was not because of Microsoft; it was because of guys like the ones who came up with XTree. With this wonderful little utility developed by a fairly small company, a user could get even more value out of their DOS-based PC. All a user had to do was sit down at your computer and type in "XTREE" at the command prompt and the computer would present the user with a visual display of all of the subdirectories on the drive. It was simple and brilliant. It completely cut out the aforementioned string of commands.

These were the kinds of innovators that were constantly enhancing DOS, and Gates never missed an opportunity to remind people of this fact. He would say that buying DOS today was an investment in software that would be written tomorrow to do things that were unimaginable.

Underneath the surface Gates was pushing his own network effect. The more people were writing software for DOS, the more valuable DOS became to end users, which prompted more users to buy DOS. Whether or not the new

---

[29] Although XTree was a real company, the example presented in this chapter is not necessarily what happened to XTree in real life.

software was commercially successful for its developers, Microsoft still benefitted from the network effect. DOS offered simply more value to end users because they had options on what software they wanted to run. The more consumers who purchased DOS-based machines, the larger the installed base and therefore more potentially lucrative it became for software developers to write for DOS. It's that same old positive feedback cycle all over again. And by the mid-80s the cycle was in full bloom and rapidly reaching the point of network lockout. Although DOS was an inferior operating system in a number of ways – in particular its 640K limit on memory usage – by the time developers needed to move past that 640K limit it was too late. DOS had already achieved a critical mass; so if the software development company wanted to reach the mass market it would find a way to work within the limits set by the DOS architecture. There was really very little choice in the matter. It was a virtuous cycle that created network lockout with DOS sitting at the center.

This mirrors the story of Wal-Mart almost to the letter up to this point. But no one ever called Sam Walton "Samgattus of Borg," even though Wal-Mart was routinely accused of destroying Main Street stores across the country. Gates received this dubious accolade because of what he and Microsoft did next.

Let's revisit the example of XTree above. Developers like the XTree guys would walk off the stage after Bill Gates has just claimed that they were the real value of DOS and greet thronging venture capitalists lining up to dole out millions of dollars for them to grow their product. So far so good.

What happens next is not so good for XTree. Following our theoretical speech by Gates, the XTree team bounds off the stage convinced they are set for life. Unfortunately, Microsoft has other plans. As the operating system sitting at the center of the entire value chain, Microsoft can be reasonably sure that nearly every XTree customer is also a Microsoft customer. Perhaps XTree had even taken Microsoft up on its generous offer to help them market their product by including coupons and other marketing material in the package with every copy of DOS sold.

From its vantage point, where it holds an immense informational advantage over the partners in the supply chain, Microsoft can view the market and makes a fateful decision for the folks at XTree. Rather than continue to partner with them and others in the file management utility sector, Microsoft reasons that everyone who uses DOS should really be using XTree, so they decide to enter the market with a competing product. To make matters worse for the other participants in that sector and in keeping with its aggressive, low-cost pricing model, Microsoft decides to give away their file management utility for free to users of DOS.

All hail the Borg as the fourth E – exterminate – is introduced into the vernacular of demand data dominance. Of course, our theoretical XTree example is merely meant to demonstrate the strategy that Gates and company would use countless more times in the following years as they absorbed their best partners into their value chain and exterminated scores of erstwhile partners.

Once Microsoft was ready to drop the fourth E on a partner or set of partners, it followed a fairly predictable pattern. It simply purchased a small vendor in the sector, almost never electing to acquire a market leader. For example, when Microsoft decided to enter the encyclopedia market in 1993 it acquired the non-exclusive rights to the Funk & Wagnall's.[30] Once they had a toehold position in a market, Microsoft focused on low price and ease of use. This drove wider market acceptance and allowed them to create miniature versions of DOS's positive feedback cycle and dominate market after market.

I have theorized about this strategy of buying relatively small players in each market. Having participated in more than several dozen software acquisitions over the years, my general theory goes as follows: the number one player in the market tends to grossly over-value their position in an acquisition. The number two player is focused on beating number one, much like Kmart and Sear's ill-fated relationship. The number three player will always take the call and may be genuinely interested, but as soon as you

---

[30] Wikipedia entry: Encarta: "Microsoft had originally approached Encyclopædia Britannica, the gold standard of encyclopedias for over a century, in the 1980s, but it declined, believing its print media sales would be hurt; however the Benton Foundation was forced to sell Encyclopædia Britannica, Inc. at below book value in 1996 when the print sales could no longer compete with Encarta...."

hang up with them they are on the phone with the top two players trying to bid up the price of the acquisition. But the number four player and beyond realize they have a long way to go before they catch number one. Generally they are dismissed by their larger peers and someone like Microsoft can explain how once they are in the fold, together they will destroy the other participants and seize the entire markets.

I would imagine the folks at Funk & Wagnall's experienced a bit of schadenfreude watching the blue bloods at Encyclopedia Britannica go down. This probably goes for all the companies Microsoft acquired over the years that helped them exterminate the likes of IBM's OS/2 as well as desktop applications like Lotus 1-2-3, Word Perfect, Harvard Graphics, etc.

As distasteful as this cut-throat business strategy may be to those on the receiving end, it has created immense wealth for Microsoft's shareholders. This method allows other companies to assume the risk of developing new lines of business while the operating system (or anyone in the position to dominate demand data) can swoop in at any time and commoditize the service line into the operating system, thereby appropriating the benefits of increasing numbers of end users and ultimately increasing revenue for itself. It would be as if Wal-Mart had looked at their sales data and seen that Product A was the highest seller in their stores nationwide. So they would go and buy a rather small competitor to Product A and market it more effectively in their stores. Perhaps using their sales and marketing advantage, Wal-Mart goes even further and dramatically undercuts the price of the good in a deliberate attempt to drive their partners out of business. Then they could absorb the manufacturer's business into their own value chain.

That is what Microsoft did, but with 90% of the operating system market share rather than Wal-Mart's 30%. Basically, the company outsourced risk in a period of punctuated equilibrium. Everyone was trying different things, with some succeeding and most failing. All the while Microsoft simply sat back and encouraged the risk taking. Once partner companies identified a significant market, Microsoft swooped in and either assimilated the functionality into the operating system or competed in the market with their own low-priced version.

Lotus 1-2-3 had to convince people to use spreadsheets, and Word Perfect had to get them to grow comfortable with word processing, and both eventually captured 85+% of their respective markets, but Microsoft just had to convince people to switch to their "suite" of products. Despite Lotus 1-2-3's and WordPerfect's dominant market share in their respective areas, Microsoft's control of the overall demand data proved to be the crucial factor. This is not to say Microsoft didn't add value in the process. One of their greatest contributions to application software came with their ability to standardize the user interface to a great degree across all the applications in their family of products. And of course they offered their products at a fraction of the prices of the market leaders, and within years had run both of them out of business.

This is another excellent example of the importance of controlling the demand data, which led to market dominance. Microsoft could price their products much lower than competitors since they could avoid customer acquisition costs, as their partners' customers were already on their platform. Ultimately the only real barrier to entry in the software market proved to be access to the demand data for a critical mass of end users, and Microsoft, as the operating system, always had the most end users. They used their position to enter new markets very effectively. This didn't endear them to large swaths of the industry, but Microsoft would argue that their aggression has benefitted the consumers with lower-cost, more integrated and user-friendly software.

Those are the four E's of demand data as implemented by Microsoft: embrace, empower, extend and exterminate. It is important to note that this process is not by any means relegated to the software market. Any organization who acquires a critical mass of demand data arguably should be in a position to execute across all four E's if they want to do it. Once a company has reached this nexus of demand data, they are almost by definition in a position to use that information to absorb extensions of the supply chain. I'm not saying that it's good or bad; it just is. And it certainly isn't a new idea. At the turn of the 20th century John D. Rockefeller used similar tactics to grow his own fortune and those of his company Standard Oil to the point where the U.S. government itself felt threatened and took action.

Rockefeller's antics make Billgatus of Borg look like a weenie.

The point of all of this with regard to the Fourth Shock is that the use of demand data to dominate markets is not a gentlemanly game. Companies like Wal-Mart have done a very good job of creating a good business while sticking within the parameters of the first three E's. They have created meaningful profit without having to crush their supply chain. Although they have been reviled by many in the press for hurting smaller businesses, they have not made a habit of cutting the throats of their partners. Quite to the contrary, they have created a reasonably healthy symbiotic relationship with their suppliers.

However, as the world shifts from a supply chain-centric view of reaction – a sell something do something model – to influencing the consumer at the point-of-purchase and influencing demand before a sale is made, companies in a position to gain an advantage through demand data can enhance their profitability in a number of ways. One approach could be to emulate Enron and trade around your informational advantage to create new profit streams off the same set of assets. A second could be to use the three E's to help your partners be more successful and extend your supply chain even further, sharing in the wealth like Wal-Mart. Or you can use that information to aggressively attack your most successful partners and absorb their value into your value chain like Microsoft does.

The bottom line is that demand data is not a nice-to-have. If you don't have it, you are in a very vulnerable position. Companies that fail to capture demand data and learn to use it in an *effective and timely* manner may find themselves at the tender mercies of their partners and/or competitors. As the old saying goes, "keep your friends close and your enemies closer." A company's most important partners in the extended supply chain of the Third Shock can quickly become its worst nightmare if that partner controls access to the customer and has a better understanding of demand data. Therefore it is imperative that businesses understand where they fit in the supply-demand information chain and make sure that they can secure their position in it.

Chapter IX: Unique Demand Data - The Holy Grail of Sustainable Competitive Advantage

"Never memorize what you can look up..."
- Albert Einstein

Channeling my inner Einstein is a passion of mine, although I can't say I am terribly successful at it. It drives my wife a little crazy at times but in any conversation I will "google" anything and everything on my Blackberry that I am not sure I completely understand or know. Based on the content of the opening quote for this chapter, if Einstein was alive today Google might well be the thing that would most amaze him. The ability to look up just about any piece of information the human race has ever generated, no matter

143

how insightful or moronic, is almost worthy of "Shock" status in and of itself.

As the second sentence of this chapter clearly demonstrates, Google is so popular and powerful it has become a verb in the same vein as FedEx and Xerox. The company's name has become synonymous with its function in the eyes of the world. Every day, millions and millions of people google hundreds of millions of times. Remarkably, the company recently passed the *trillion* point mark in indexing of unique URLs.

When you are within walking distance and available use of a computer or any other device capable of connecting to the Internet, and any question comes to mind – be it related to a past war or the time of a movie showing or really anything – is your first instinct not to jump online and "google it?" How did Google rise to this point in our culture and how could it possibly relate to our spirited discussion about the power of demand data? Undoubtedly the company's pioneering ideas on how to find things on the ever increasing content base of the Internet propelled it to become the Web's dominant search engine, but the company's sustainable advantage lies in their *unique* historical database of user and behavioral information.

Google began as a few ideas in the minds of two Stanford graduate students, Sergey Brin and Larry Page. In its early years the Internet was cluttered and disorganized and expanding wildly. Pursuant to his Ph.D., Brin had begun interacting with the field of data mining, which is basically the field of intelligently extracting information from large amounts of data. Brin and some of his fellow students were curious as to how data mining techniques could be applied to the young and disorganized Internet.

While a great number of people were warming up to the Internet by starting to communicate through email, the lack of knowledge about the Internet's functions and capabilities were stifling. Beginning to experiment with data mining, Brin and his colleagues found that searching on the Internet was inordinately difficult and inefficient. Search engines of the day were primitive, often returning results that made little to no sense at all and were seemingly random. This frustrated end users and made the Internet seem amazingly vast but almost pointless.

While Brin was focused on data mining, Larry Page began working with Internet searching as well. Using the fairly new search engine AltaVista, Page spotted an untapped resource. Along with its search results, AltaVista would report the number of links associated with any result item. As many of you know by now, links are reference points on a web page or in a document on which a user can click to be directed to external or internal pages or documents. This appeared to most people at the time as a nice added piece of information, but nothing more. Page began to theorize about web link analysis, and went so far as to surprise his advisor by claiming that, in a move necessary to more fully begin analyzing the possibilities within links, he would download the entire World Wide Web to his desktop.

Given the similarities of their projects, Page and Brin joined forces in the effort to analyze links. Page's original theory was based on the analogy that web links are like citations in an academic paper. The more respected and pertinent an article or scholarly piece of work is, the more apt other writers will be to cite it in the bodies of their work. If this concept is applied to web pages, the more links a page has from other sites, the more likely it is to be pertinent and worthwhile.

This idea represented a very different approach from the search engines of the day as nearly every one of them was based pretty much entirely on simply matching values. Results would come back based on finding matching words on a website, but that website might just contain those words, having nothing to do with the actual topic. Furthermore, it wasn't long before websites figured out how search engines worked and simply "seeded" web pages and sites with keywords in order to get search engines to pick them up and list them. In many if not most cases these seeded pages had little or nothing to do with the keyword. This practice once again led to frustrated end users and the perception that the Internet was mostly filled with useless information.

Under this model the best pertinent website might come up first or be mixed in with a number of results far down the page. There was simply no set organization. Page theorized that if his idea could actually be applied, an inherent ranking system would take place that should result in far superior results. Initial tests run on Page's "desktop

The Fourth Shock

World Wide Web" showed the theory to be sound, as search results based on the number of links to any specific page did appear to deliver superior relevance.

Page then took the idea an important step further. He realized that just as a citation from a published professor would be more indicative of merit than a citation from a high school student, a link from a major website such as Amazon.com would be much more important than a link from a small personal site. Links, he decided, should have differing weights. What the system became was an algorithm for analyzing links based on how many links a page received, the quality or importance of the pages doing the linking, the relevance of the search keywords on the page, and the number of visits to the page Google had been able to record. There are other factors to how the algorithm works as well, but in order to prevent manipulation of the system many of these factors are still withheld by Google.

Nodding to his own surname, the link-rating system was called "PageRank" and it served as one of the first building blocks of Google. The new search engine would produce results ranked on the number of links and the quality or importance of sources of those links.

To put PageRank into use, Page and Brin originally used a fairly primitive search engine that they called BackRub, because of its nature of analyzing incoming links from web pages, called backlinks. In 1997 they decided to change the name to Google, a shortened and accidentally misspelled derivative of the enormously large numerical term googolplex.

The Fourth Shock

The Google search engine was first made available internally to the staff and student body of Stanford, where it was wildly popular. Less than a year after that, Google was incorporated with a work space in a garage and a $100 thousand check from Sun Microsystems cofounder Andy Bechtolsheim. As Internet usage continued to rise, word got out through sources like *PC Magazine* that there was a search engine that was producing uniquely relevant results. From that point forward the company grew at a furious rate.

On August 19, 2004, the company's rapid rise culminated in an enormously successful IPO. It has been estimated that over 1000 employees of the company became instant millionaires that day, not to mention a couple of billionaires. As of this writing, the company's market capitalization stood at just over $155 billion and posted annual revenue in 2008 of $21 billion.

No doubt much of Google's value stems from its steady growth, but that growth in many ways is driven by a very unique asset that simply cannot be replicated by any other company in the world. That asset is a truly unique set of demand data.

Although the company boasts some of the most sophisticated and battle tested algorithms designed to deliver the best possible search results on the web today, it stands to reason that competitors with the financial and intellectual wherewithal of Microsoft can find ways to match Google's mathematical prowess. But what cannot be matched is Google's historical database of detailed consumer behavior on the web going back over a decade.

That information could be stolen, but it can never be replicated.

Google's single most important asset is their database. The simple reason is that people are always doing different things on the web. Maybe last year you searched for a big screen TV and this year you are looking for a deal on a new iPod. But you rarely search for the same thing day in and day out. Because Google has a head start on everyone else in the world who wants to compete with them, their amazing algorithms will have more data to run against than anyone else's. Combine this with their market leading position which continues to give them more behavioral data on a daily basis than anyone else in the market today, and you get the justification for a $155 billion value.

Google has indexed over 1 trillion URLs, insuring that users who use their search engine get some of the most efficient and valuable results. This in turn insures that Google is constantly capturing increasing amounts of information from those users every time they visit. Data about the way they search, surf, behave and consume is all added to the company's repository of consumer data and is used to keep advertisers constantly spending the money that supports Google.

And what a repository of data. From the moment Larry Page decided to download the entire web onto his desktop, Google has had to be obsessive about data storage. Their strategy for storing the absurd amount of real-time demand data they capture every day has been to use cheaper, commodity computers clustered in intelligent ways rather than the most expensive equipment. The heart of this ongoing effort is what is called the Google File System.

The Google File System divides all data files into 64-megabyte chunks stored on nodes, which are simply commodity computers. Nodes are divided into Chunkservers and a Master node. Chunkservers store the 64-megabyte files, and each of those files is replicated a number of times throughout the system to provide availability if one file becomes inaccessible. Master nodes store all the metadata – basically the information that keeps the Chunkservers working and in order. It stores maps of the chunk locations and the locations of their copies. It stores information about the processes of the different chunks, and aids in replicating a chunk if the number of its copies have fallen too low. And the Chunkservers are constantly sending updates to the Master nodes to keep everything current.

While Google's storage of indexed web site data is what is sought after by its users, its users' data is what is useful to Google and to advertisers. It is another one of those damned virtuous cycles that keep popping up. The more user data Google can gather and use, the better their search results and the more value they can provide to advertisers. And the better the search results the more user data Google will be able to gather.

The company stores user data in many different ways. One way is click tracking, in which they log all the navigational clicks of all users of their services. Information is also stored on every website visited as a result of a Google search. Information about the search itself is stored, such as result pages, country code domain, the query, the IP address, the language, and the number of results. They also store cookies, which are small pieces of text that contain information such as a user's preferences, shopping cart information, and personal information that has been provided. Google stores a great deal of user information, to an extent that it has become controversial to some. It is easy to see, however, the ways in which certain stored user data is helpful to Google's operations.

One of the main reasons for storing user data is that it helps Google to refine and improve their search engine. For instance analysts look at how often users skipped to second, third, fourth, or latter results for a certain search to see if the way the search was conducted on their end should be modified. It also helps with misspellings. If someone searches "bnanas" but the great majority of previous similar searches in their logs read "bananas," an alert would pop up asking if the user meant the latter.

The implementation of cookies storing user preferences helps facilitate advertising to users. In the same vein Google employs software in their Gmail service that scans personal emails for keywords and in turn employs those keywords to provide advertisements on the side of the screen. This type of handling of user-generated data is the core of Google's money-making process.

Google uses all of this user data to drive the value of its main source of revenue - Google AdWords. AdWords refers to the system they have set up that involves the pay-per-click purchase and ongoing auction of text-based advertisement space on the right-hand side of a Google results page.

The pay-per-click portion of buying an ad on Google involves the key words that an advertiser wants to trigger their ad and the maximum amount they would be willing to pay per click received. Google then proceeds to use a plethora of data to choose what ads will be shown in what order. For instance an ad will receive greater prominence the more it has been clicked on in the past. The relevance of the advertiser and the quality of the landing page they are trying to advertise play into consideration as well.

While the cost per click for a client to run an ad can fluctuate depending on what is being advertised, Google does not actually set the price themselves. The prices are governed by what advertisers are willing to pay at any given time – in a constant online auction. Advertisers are constantly bidding to win spots on the never ending results pages of Google's searchers. This constant auction system benefits both Google and advertisers. For one, advertisers can bid as much on a particular ad space as it is worth to them, and the winning bid gets the space. For Google, this cuts out the process of determining what price advertisers *would* be willing to pay and automatically guarantees them the highest price possible. The auction system also allows smaller clients and companies to advertize just as easily as huge ones with bigger budgets. Smaller advertisers can bid higher on particular ad spaces of interest to them, or they can modify their keywords to purchase ads with lower-cost results.

In a system like this one it is easy to see the extreme importance of consumer data. Companies can keep track of the ads on which they spent money and see which ones actually got clicked on, and then which of those clicked on produced actual buyers of their products. They could then put more money into more profitable ads and pull the weaker ones. The system also brought into focus more nuanced aspects of advertising to the massive online community. For instance, ads placed on results pages for the search terms "consolidate school loans" may fetch more click-throughs than ones place for "consolidate student loans," making the former a higher priced ad. Users searching "alarm clocks" might be more prone to end up buying than those that searched "alarm clock." In many cases, larger companies go as far as dedicating employees to the sole task of keeping up with this kind of consumer data and constantly bidding appropriately.

While the highest bid in an auction for a particular ad is the biggest factor in positioning it in the results, it is not the only factor. Also taken into account is the previous success of the ad, which is defined as the number of times it has been clicked on in the past. So Google even stores behavioral information about its clients, not just its search users. If that isn't comprehensive storage, I don't know what is. It allows for advertising that is not of the broad, billboard type, but rather the type that reaches out to the user at a point at which they are already interested, similar to and often exactly like the kind of point-of-purchase advertising on which many companies can thrive.

Google's exploitation of user data does not stop there or exist only inside of AdWords. In 2007, Google acquired DoubleClick, which allows clients to track and report on online advertising campaigns. It reports on a user's browser, operating system, Internet service provider, bandwidth, and more using the IP address or the cookies stored on the user's machine. In a classic move of empowering their supply chain, Google also offers as a free service Google Analytics. Google Analytics is a resource that generates information about visitors to a website. It tracks all visitors that were referred from someplace else, such as email links or search engines and reports their information to the subscriber. Clients of AdWords can use Google Analytics as an easier way of tracking how the advertisements they have placed are reaching Internet users and whether the ads are being clicked or not.

The impetus for Sergey Brin and Larry Page to create Google was data management. They saw the massive amount of data forming on the Internet and the lack of any meaningfully efficient avenues of searching through it. By indexing that data and making it available to users in the most relevant way, they aggregated a huge base of users. Google began collecting data on the behavior of those users before anyone else, resulting in a base of data that was proprietary to the company. In Google's case it would be called first mover advantage. The ironic thing about first mover advantage in today's intensely connected world is that it can often serve as nothing more than a means of alerting more established competitors to a market opportunity.

But this is not the case when it comes to unique demand data. In the realm of data storage, first mover advantage is still alive and well. Google's lucky break was that they started collecting user data before anyone else. Their algorithms can be copied. Better functions could be created, and probably have. There are probably search engines floating around the Internet that work better than Google's. But while someone might be able to duplicate or even exceed the capabilities of their algorithms, no one can touch the mass of unique and proprietary data they have aggregated, and that is what has made Google worth $155 billion. Like Microsoft with its operating system that was not necessarily the best but gained a critical mass, Google doesn't have to have the best search engine; they already have the best data.

This is one major way in which demand data capture will change with the onset of mobility. Demand data is immensely important to acquire in the first place, and for Google the most important aspect of their data was that it was unique and proprietary. Their indexing of user behavior data from the fledgling days of their search engine put them in an advantageous spot to which no one else has been able to catch up.

Think about the amount of data Proctor & Gamble could amass if they were getting real-time demand data from billions of consumers swiping their cell phones over bar codes and other unique identifiers and interacting with objects in the real world rather than only on the web. Rather than getting their delayed demand data from Wal-Mart or from IRI, P&G could benefit immensely from data generated from the interactions with consumers on a global basis. Some of these interactions might result in additional sales and others might be missed opportunities, but both would provide unique data points from which to better understand overall consumer demand and adjust their sales and marketing strategies accordingly. If done right, P&G would begin to collect proprietary consumer demand data for all of their many products, and use that information to improve performance across the board. The next chapter explores this in detail, but the implications are enormous for the entire global supply chain in practically every market.

This is why companies need to get on top of demand data accumulation now, instead of five years from now. The unique data that can be generated through interactions with consumers must be integrated with more traditional means of analysis and leveraged effectively. But like Google's unique database, it will be the company with the best reach to consumers across the market and the most unique historical data that will be in a position to gain the insights necessary to thrive in the Fourth Shock.

Chapter X: The Proactive Supply Chain

"In time of profound change, the Learners inherit the earth, while the Learned find themselves beautifully equipped to deal with a world that no longer exists."
-- Eric Hofer

One tidbit of wisdom I have picked up over the years is that a keen sense of the obvious doesn't make someone a visionary. And the obvious today is that for the first time in human history more than half the world's population carries a two-way communication device. This *will* have an impact on the way the world works. By way of comparison to the 4.1 billion active mobile phone subscriptions, there are approximately 850 million active personal computers, 1.5 billion televisions, 1.5 billion Internet nodes and 1.4 billion credit cards in use in the world today.

The Fourth Shock

This astonishing market potential hasn't gone unnoticed by the world's best and brightest technological minds. Reminiscent of the mid-1990s and the excitement surrounding the Internet, Silicon Valley and the world's other hi-tech havens are aggressively betting that the power of the mobile device is untapped and that it will be the arena that generates the next household names in technology. There will be many misfires and false starts, but it is only a matter of time before the commercialization of mobility starts to have the same impact on business that the commercialization of the Internet did in the 1990s.

From the earliest days of the First Shock's digital data, through the heady days of the Internet bubble and the Third Shock, manufacturers and retailers have collectively spent hundreds of billions of dollars developing the global supply chain in order to maximize profits by reducing inventories and accelerating their response to shifts in consumer preferences. Companies have tweaked every variable; from the acquisition of raw materials all the way through to the strategic placement of goods on the retailer's shelves and everything in between, the global supply chain has wrung meaningful efficiencies across the board. However, the advent of the ubiquitous mobile device enables businesses to take the next logical step in the continued extension of the supply chain – influencing the consumer at the point-of-purchase.

The point-of-purchase (POP) is not the same as the point-of-sale (POS). The POS is the record of a transaction – sell something, do something. It is one end of the supply chain pipeline for every business. The POP by contrast goes beyond the POS and is the point at which a consumer is considering a purchase but has not yet made one. She is standing in an aisle or sitting in front of a computer screen actively looking for a good or service. She may be only window shopping or she may be focused on a particular product or category, but she is an active lead. What is guiding her decision making process as she decides between purchasing Product A or Product B?

Regardless of whether she is a sophisticated shopper extensively researching a buying decision or simply an impulse buyer, corporations spend hundreds of billions of dollars a year on advertising hoping to influence her decisions at the POP. The largest 200 consumer product goods companies alone spend over $50 billion in advertising and marketing annually just to be "top of mind" at that fateful moment called the POP.

In Chapter VI we made references to a certain nervous cow in Kansas. But what if that cow decided to do something about his precarious position? Since 1995, cows have been doing just that. In that year the Chick-fil-A cows launched their long running campaign to get people to "Eat Mor Chikin." It is a blatant attempt at self preservation by the cows and an even more blatant attempt by Chick-fil-A to get people into their stores buying their offerings.

It works. Advertising has been shaping attitudes and opinions about everything from politicians to dental floss for decades. Despite advertising's success – or perhaps because of it – the industry operates in pretty much the same manner as it has for the last fifty years. It is a world of branding and messages and jingles and coupons. The whole industry can be summed up in one of my favorite sayings, "make 'em laugh, make 'em think, give 'em pleasure and you got them." However, accountability in the advertising industry is uncertain at best and results are often measured in months and years. "Did our Super Bowl ad have the desired affect?" Wait six months to find out.

Just as the First Shock was instrumental in making "just-in-time" manufacturing a reality that was continually fine tuned through the next two Shocks, mobility and mobile devices, the agents of change in the Fourth Shock, will usher in the era of "just-in-time" marketing and accountable advertising. If deregulation was the catalyst that created the chaos and uncertainty necessary for Enron to benefit from information advantages, mobility will act as a global deregulatory force for advertising and marketing and create unprecedented opportunities and risks for every business no matter how big or small.

Mobility makes it possible to exert some last minute influence on a consumer at the exact moment when businesses would most like to do so. Today the technology already exists to allow a consumer to enter a text code or even wave her cell phone over a bar code and begin real-time interactions with the manufacturer of the product. With the proper technology in place a manufacturer can communicate directly with a consumer at the POP and shape her decision making process.

The Fourth Shock

Let's assume our theoretical shopper is in the market for a 42" High Definition TV. She strolls through the aisles of the local Best Buy® and sees a display ad in front of a Sony® model that encourages her to use her cell phone and enter the text code 43200. She does so and is instantly presented with a menu of available interactions she can perform. For example, take some time to review the following list of options that could be displayed on her cell phone:

1) Click here to dial a Sony sales representative who can explain in detail the benefits of this model
2) Click here to view an article from Consumer Reports comparing this model to other models
3) Click here to receive a special offer from Sony on this model if you buy today
4) Click here to get the best price from Amazon.com for this model delivered to you

Obviously, this list could contain many other options. If she chooses number one, the call would get routed to a call center where a Sony representative, using the company's CRM (customer relationship management) software would identify the caller from her cell phone number. Sony would also be able to know her location because the text code she entered or bar code she swiped would be unique to that particular store. The cell tower from which the phone call was placed would also be available. In addition, any other information about this individual that Sony has from previous interactions could be there as well.

The agent could then offer to answer any questions and/or launch into a sales pitch as to why this model is the best choice for this consumer. My guess is most consumers would avoid all of this personal interaction because it is harder to say "no" to a person than it is to walk away from a computer generated offer. So let's assume our theoretical consumer opts for number three.

First, notice the specific wording on the link: "Click here to receive a special offer from Sony on this model if you buy today." It says "special offer" because using existing technology Sony could vary the offer based on any number of factors and each offer could be different *all the way down to an individual consumer.*

At its most basic level, once a consumer clicks on link number three the real-time demand information would be routed to Sony's internal systems. To process this "interaction," Sony would look at the local and regional supply situations and determine if an extra discount is warranted. This would be done by rules set up in advance. A simple example of such a rule would be: "If Product A has X amount or greater of inventory in warehouse B, offer Y% discount. If Product A is less than X amount of inventory, offer a coupon for Product B" (perhaps in this case a Blue Ray disc player).

From there the questions really start to fly. How would Sony determine the optimal price discount based on various supply/demand situations? Does Sony have any information about this consumer and/or demographic that they could use to influence her behavior? Can Sony predict her next purchases with reasonable accuracy assuming she makes the purchase? What if she doesn't make the purchase, was this entire interaction a complete waste of time? Can Sony resolve an inventory problem in another location by offering a bigger discount to have the consumer go there to pick up the product? And remember, all of this has to happen in seconds.

Second, note that the link can be custom tailored to this *individual* consumer. During this interaction we have captured her cell phone number, cell tower location, store location and many other possible pieces of data. Looking into our CRM system we may note that she has purchased a number of items from Sony over the years and she may be a member of Sony's loyalty club. If that is the case, perhaps the company would want to offer her something more substantial than a less loyal customer. The point is Sony can vary the offer down to the individual's identity.

Also note that number four allows the consumer to contact Amazon and get the best price available *there* rather than in the Best Buy in which she is shopping. Why would that option be there? Because it is a perfect example of the third E of demand data dominance, extending the value chain for the customer. Perhaps Sony gets a better rate of return from Amazon than from Best Buy. Furthermore, what if Best Buy has in-store brands that compete directly with Sony, similar to the situation in Costco for example where they actively compete with their partners a la

The Fourth Shock

Microsoft's Fourth E via their in-store Kirkland Signature brand?

If retailers are going to compete directly with manufacturers with in-store and generic brands, it seems reasonable to allow manufacturers to compete with retailers by giving consumers choices on their mobile phone at the POP. Additionally, Sony could redirect the consumer to a different store in the area in which a supply situation warrants an extra discount. For example, let's assume our shopper is at Best Buy in Norwalk, CT. Sony looks at its supply chain data as part of this interaction and sees that the Best Buy in a nearby town is oversupplied with the same model and is increasing inventory costs for both Sony and Best Buy.

In this scenario Sony and/or Best Buy could send a coupon to the consumer noting that if she is willing to drive 30 miles to the other location she could save an additional X dollars. Compare all of this to today's in-store advertising models designed to influence consumers at the POP. Retailers and manufacturers are reduced to 5x8 cards and in-aisle gimmicks and have very limited insight into how effective such efforts really are. With mobility and individual consumer interactions, once a consumer initiates the dialogue every aspect of it can be captured, stored, analyzed and acted upon.

None of the above is fantasy. The technology, infrastructure and consumer comfort with mobile devices are all in place. It is a short leap from here to mass adoption of these capabilities. This is the second critical aspect of the

The Fourth Shock

Fourth Shock – companies *must develop systems today* that will allow them to interact with consumers in real-time. Modern mobile devices' innate capabilities enable businesses to dynamically create any number of interactive capabilities which will generate, capture and transmit detailed, real-time demand data to consumers at the POP.

These direct consumer interactions will constitute a new kind of demand data that must be integrated in real-time with traditional sources of supply and demand data and acted upon. Even more importantly, this demand data generated from these interactions is *unique* and proprietary. Just like Google's immense value is driven from unique information about consumer interactions on the Web, a manufacturer or retailer can capture similar data as a direct interaction with a consumer.

Of course, there is always the possibility that our consumer asks for Sony's best offer, receives a coupon good for the next 60 minutes, and chooses not to act on it. Perhaps she had the same type of interactions with Panasonic and opted to buy that brand instead, or perhaps she simply opted to do nothing at this time. Sony wouldn't necessarily know what she did if she didn't act on the offer, but they would know something very valuable nonetheless – the fact that she chose not to act on the offer. This "negative" data is as interesting and arguably just as valuable as any point-of-sale data after a transaction. Even more importantly, it is proprietary to Sony. Only they know that they made an offer and it was refused. Do that a few thousand times a day and you will quickly find demand trends that others simply have no access to.

This means manufacturers will no longer be insulated from consumers by their distribution channels; for the first time they will know firsthand about end users' preferences and reactions to factory promotions and advertising campaigns.

Imagine if you could recognize a shift in consumer tastes as it occurs in real-time rather than waiting weeks, months or years as is the case today. Imagine if you owned a company that can capture a meaningful amount of global demand data on any item long before the other participants in the supply chain could. How would that change your business – advertising, marketing, purchasing, promotions, and distribution?

Nothing in the preceding paragraphs comes from the realm of science fiction. The technology exists today to do all of the above. Reminiscent of the early days of the PC and the Internet, the only thing missing is a mass market for this kind of functionality. Predictive analytics, pricing analytics, behavioral analytics and numerous other technologies will sit atop demand data and constantly sharpen a manufacturer's or retailer's real-time view of consumer preferences and optimize one-on-one interactions with them.

As mobility goes mainstream the business world will shift from a predominantly reactive, supply chain focused view of the consumer to a more proactive, demand centric view. The *Proactive Supply Chain* will use information across a company's existing infrastructure to interact with a consumer at the point-of-purchase and optimize the likelihood that she will purchase its products or services. Furthermore, the outcome of these interactions will be stored as unique demand data resources that can be used to constantly improve a company's understanding of demand trends and refine their responses to them.

Chapter XI: Preparing to Thrive in the Fourth Shock

"If you are not outraged by the implications of quantum physics, you don't understand it."

- Niels Bohr

Arguably, the easiest sales job in the world was selling SAP[31] software in the early 1990's. The pitch was ironclad and the price tag was nothing short of astronomical. As a friend of mine who sold SAP at the time poetically phrased

---

[31] Wikipedia entry: "SAP AG (ISIN: DE0007164600, FWB: SAP, NYSE: SAP) is a multinational software development and consulting corporation, which provides enterprise software applications and support to businesses of all sizes globally. ... SAP is (as of 2009) the largest software enterprise in Europe and the fourth largest software enterprise in the world.

it, "It was a baby seal bashing." And the reason was simple
– Y2K.[32]

Perhaps a brief history lesson is in order. Before the
world reached the year 1000, huge crowds formed in St.
Peter's Square in Vatican City on the night of December
31st, cowering in their poorly made shoes for what they
were sure was the end of the world. Unfortunately for many
of the true believers, the sun rose the following day and it
was back to the glamour of the Middle Ages for them all.
Silly Medieval peasants! Of course, the more things
change...

One thousand years later the citizens of earth held their
collective breath as the clocks on computers around the
world rolled forward to the year 2000. Predictions of
apocalyptic disasters failed to materialize, but the very real
threat of the Y2K bug had the unintended effect of laying
the groundwork for transformation of the enterprise
technology markets for years to come.

From a sales perspective, Y2K was an incredible boon.
As any enterprise salesperson worth their fat commissions
will tell you, there are only two things that will get people
to write ridiculously large checks – greed and fear. As

---

[32] Wikipedia entry: "The Year 2000 problem (also known
as the Y2K problem, the millennium bug, the Y2K bug, or simply
Y2K) was a notable problem for both digital (computer-related)
and non-digital documentation and data storage situations which
resulted from the practice of abbreviating a four-digit year to two
digits."

The Fourth Shock

Machiavelli would undoubtedly agree, of these two fear is much more effective. And Y2K provided fear by the train load.

The Y2K threat came from fairly modest beginnings. Back in the earliest days of the computing era, information storage was extremely limited and very expensive. Therefore, in order to save time and money, programmers chose to indicate the year with only two digits. For example the year 1942 was designated only as "42." As systems evolved and additional layers of complexity were added onto existing programs, it became difficult to change the underlying code, so the two-digit year designation became somewhat of a standard. This continued to be the case even long after the cost of information storage had declined significantly. By the 1960s, many programmers recognized the problem, but they easily rationalized away the issue by convincing themselves that the technology of that time would no longer be in use in the year 2000. As the world entered the final decade of the millennium, concerns grew that computers systems around the world would crash due to their inability to understand that the year "00" was 2000 and not 1900.

The potential threat of this problem cannot be overstated. Computer systems contain millions and millions of lines of code, and sorting through the arcane coding of now defunct programming languages was the software equivalent of correcting grammar in ancient Egyptian hieroglyphics. And even once the modifications were made, the testing process was extremely complicated

The Fourth Shock

as changes in one part of the code could have unintended and potentially ruinous effects in other parts. But code wasn't the only problem.

Microchips, which were embedded in almost every modern appliance, product and machine that used electronic technology (e.g. cars, cash registers, home entertainment equipment and gas pumps), were also vulnerable to the Y2K bug. Many of these items used a time/date/year sequence that, if not able to recognize year 2000, could cause them to fail. Further compounding the potential problem was the fact that information seldom operated alone. Energy, food, and financial services are prime examples of the interconnected nature of computer systems, where failure in one component of the supply chain could send shock waves through the entire system. Ironically, perhaps the best example of the interconnected nature of the modern world came after Y2K had passed in the great "blackout" experienced by much of the Northeast U.S. and Canada in 2003. A problem in one power plant resulted in the rapid shut down of more than 100 power plants, including 22 nuclear reactors, and knocked out power to 50 million people over a 9,300-square-mile area stretching from New England to Michigan. This type of scenario multiplied hundreds of times drove the fear underlying Y2K

In the February 13, 1984, issue of *ComputerWorld* magazine, Paul Gillin made the first printed reference to the Y2K problem, which pretty much went unnoticed except in extremely geeky circles. However, it was another all-too-real disaster in that year that laid the psychological groundwork for the irrational fears of Y2K that were to grip CEO's the world over ten years later. That event was the Bhopal disaster in India.

"In the early hours of Monday, Dec. 3, 1984, a toxic cloud of methyl isocyanate (MIC) gas enveloped the hundreds of shanties and huts surrounding a pesticide plant in Bhopal, India. Later, as the deadly cloud slowly drifted in the cool night air through streets in surrounding sections, sleeping residents awoke, coughing, choking, and rubbing painfully stinging eyes. By the time the gas cleared at dawn, many were dead or injured. Four months after the tragedy, the Indian government reported to its Parliament that 1,430 people had died. In 1991 the official Indian government panel charged with tabulating deaths and injuries updated the count to more than 3,800 dead and approximately 11,000 with disabilities.

...The plant was operated by Union Carbide India Limited (UCIL), just over 50 percent of which was owned by Union Carbide Corporation. The first report of the disaster reached Union Carbide executives in the United States more than 12 hours after the incident. By 6:00 a.m. in the U.S., executives were gathering with technical, legal, and communications staff at the company's Danbury, Connecticut headquarters. Information was sparse but, as casualty estimates quickly climbed, the matter was soon recognized as a massive industrial disaster.

The first press inquiry came at 4:30 a.m. in the U.S., marking the beginning of a deluge that, at its peak, reached 500 calls a day for several weeks. The scope of the Bhopal tragedy made it "page one" material in the weeks and months that followed. And, as its legal, political, technological and -- above all -- human aspects were explored, it became a persistent headline into the 1990s."-

Jackson Browning Report - Union Carbide Corp.

With Bhopal still making front page news, an article written by Peter de Jager in the September 6, 1993, issue of *ComputerWorld* magazine sounded the warning bells for the potential dangers of the Y2K bug. Picked up by the mainstream press, the Y2K bug was cited as threat so powerful it would make the disaster at Bhopal look like child's play. Fear gripped CEO's of major corporations around the world as they were hit with a once-in-a-lifetime challenge that could literally threaten the world economy and even result in tragic death for countless people. To make matters worse, this threat emerged from an area that most CEO's were wholly unequipped to deal with. At the time, many if not most CEO's of large companies were not even using computers, so when Y2K suddenly thrust to the fore as a potentially ruinous threat, they were hard pressed to realistically assess its true extent.

They therefore turned to their internal technology experts who themselves were in a turf war with the business people for control of budgets. As companies attempted to deal with the Second Shock and the distribution of PCs and networking across the enterprise, they minted a new senior level role called the Chief Information Officer (CIO).[33] The Y2K threat quickly consolidated significant amounts of dollars in the hands of the information technology department (IT) and the CIO, and with those dollars came the ability to shape corporate information flows and in too many cases, overall corporate strategy.

It was into this chaotic environment the lowly SAP sales person found himself. The sales pitch went something like this: "If you don't buy my software and re-engineer your entire corporation your chemical plant in Louisiana might explode on New Year's day in the year 2000. Bhopal on the Bayou if you will. That'll be $200,000,000. Thank you for your business." Of course, you could simply replace the words "chemical plant," "Louisiana" and the pithy proposed headline for the disaster, but the end result was almost always the same – sale closed.

---

[33] At the time it was often sarcastically referred to as "Career Is Over."

The Fourth Shock

By the time Y2K hit it was one of the biggest non-events in human history. It came and went with nary an issue. Of course, SAP and its competitors argue to this day that they are a big reason why nothing happened and that the billions spent by corporations was worth every penny. Frankly, they are probably right. But without the panic mindset of Y2K the same results would have come about at a fraction of the cost.

I mention all of this as a cautionary tale to my readers. If business leaders, investors and politicians are ignorant of fundamental technological shifts occurring across the economy they can be herded like our poor Kansas cows in chapter five on their way to slaughter. Mobility and the Fourth Shock, like the three previous shocks before it, will seem to the uninitiated as a sudden event that is simultaneously exciting and terrifying. Both greed and fear will cause people to overreact, resulting in poorly planned strategies executed over unnecessarily short time frames and foolhardy, over-hyped investments with little or no real chance for success.

The inevitable onset of the Fourth Shock has already begun and the time to prepare for it is now. Mobility and its dramatic impact on the global economy will not happen overnight. Like the positive feedback cycles of the three previous shocks, demand data is rushing to the forefront of global competitive strategies, and companies that embrace these changes will secure a distinct competitive advantage. The ability to capture and store unique demand data will drive new competitive strategies and the company that can most quickly collect a critical mass of demand data will have a distinct advantage.

At its core, the Fourth Shock argues that the company or organization with the most unique demand data wins. Mobility and access to POS systems at speeds approaching real-time are the technological drivers of the Fourth Shock, but it will be the ability to combine these new real-time demand data streams with historical trends, find meaningful insights, and profit from it – all within seconds, thousands of times a day. Today there are four main obstacles every organization must overcome in order to seize the opportunities and minimize the risks associated with the Fourth Shock.

First is the pressing problem caused by the ever-increasing number of demand data feeds available to organizations. Known as "balkanization," this problem is routinely cited by CIOs as one of the most important and expensive challenges facing their organization.

Historically, demand data has come from a fairly limited number of sources. Data aggregators like Information Resources, Inc. (IRI) and AC Nielsen have built very large businesses by aggregating POS data across the globe and providing that information for a handsome fee to companies to use in enhancing their decision making. Getting this information from thousands upon thousands of retail outlets and consolidating that into an enormous data base is a substantial undertaking.

Because of this effort, it can be weeks or months between the time a transaction was recorded on a POS system and its availability to a manufacturer to gauge market performance. Therefore, if a large CPG company runs an ad campaign in a market to attack a perceived opportunity, it could be several months before the results could be discerned. From the data consumer's point of view, the slow arrival of the POS information is far from optimal, but for decades that is how it was done. Technically, IT would have to manage these large data feeds and make sure that they are not improperly used and that the data from them can get to the right people across the organization. Once the data finally gets to these business analysts they then add value to the information in the form of insightful trend analysis and the like and then push it out to various areas of the company such as sales, marketing and senior management.

Enter Retail Link from Wal-Mart. Once Wal-Mart announced that it would no longer make its POS data available to aggregators like IRI, but instead would *only* provide the information to its partners in the supply chain, it changed the game for the entire industry. Wal-Mart recognized that the proprietary demand information in their POS system provides themselves and their partners with a competitive advantage, and they were no longer willing to share it indiscriminately. An added benefit to their partners came from the fact that Wal-Mart would make the data available on a *daily* basis.

This gave Wal-Mart's suppliers the unprecedented ability to adjust strategies and react to situations in time

The Fourth Shock

frames that were unthinkable before Retail Link. Of course, this also had a negative impact on the aggregator's value proposition to their customers as a significant portion of overall sales data would no longer be available in their service.

Also impacted by this move were the internal IT departments of the partners in Wal-Mart's supply chain. Suddenly, the problem went from managing one enormous data feed to two slightly smaller, but both still gigantic, data feeds. In the IT world this is not simply a 1+1=2 problem, meaning that two feeds do not increase your headaches twofold. It is more like 4x, as mingling the data across the feeds, controlling access and managing data flows becomes much more problematic. Despite the significant pain this caused, it was still reasonably manageable by existing IT infrastructure.

Throughout the next 10 years however, more and more retailers decided to discontinue participating with the aggregators like IRI and Nielsen and have opted to offer their own POS feeds directly to their partners in the supply chain. The good news for the world is that this information is usually available far more quickly than historical methods. The bad news is that IT is being slammed with the need to manage all of these new feeds, with the resulting complexity spinning out of control and overwhelming existing methodologies and infrastructure.

Simply getting the demand data from POS systems poses a huge challenge, but an even bigger nightmare is the fact that most industries do not have standards for "tagging" data. This means Product A in the Wal-Mart feed is called 123456, but in the feed from Target Product A may be called ABCDEF. In order to get a complete picture of the POS data across both feeds it needs to be "normalized", or matched up across both feeds.

This is a daunting challenge with just two feeds, but across dozens it becomes an extremely difficult problem. A big step in the right direction would be an agreement across the major manufacturers and retailers in various industry segments to tag demand data in a universal way at the point-of-sale. However, these types of standards are notoriously difficult to implement and even when successful, take years.

But the combination of these two factors – ever-increasing numbers of retailers providing direct feeds to consumers of the demand data and the lack of standards for tagging data – are rapidly overwhelming existing systems. In the near term, this will be the biggest bottleneck in the ability of companies to acquire and leverage demand data.

A second major problem stems from the fact that mobility and the need to interact in real-time with consumers create an entirely new situation in the world. In most cases there is no infrastructure in place to do this in any meaningful way. I cannot overstate the fact that billions and billions of people are walking around with two-way communication devices that are generating entirely new kinds of real-time data every second of every day.

The battlefront for competitive advantage is shifting from reactive supply chains to proactive ones that focus as much or more on the point-of-purchase as they do on the point-of-sale. This fact adds to the complexity and challenges already being faced by companies simply trying to get POS data into their companies in an organized, usable way.

A third pressing problem is the limited ability of the people who have to use all of this demand data to learn new software applications every time a new data feed is added. This is another example of "balkanization", but this time it is the proliferation of user interfaces attached to various data sets that is spiraling out of control. Trying to get end users to learn and relearn various software packages every time a new set of data is added to the overall system is akin to trying to teach a pig to dance – it is impossible and it annoys the pig.

Back in the 1990s, I gave numerous presentations where I chided software developers for focusing more on cool technology rather than helping end users be more effective at the *real* work that companies do. Few end users have the time or the inclination to spend their careers learning how to use software, only to have it change if a data provider changes. And with the explosion of demand data resources being made available to organizations, this problem will need to be addressed.

All three of these challenges will inhibit an organization's ability to efficiently capture, store, analyze and act on real-time demand data. However, the most critical function organizations need to implement is a comprehensive knowledge management solution in order to most effectively hone a long term demand data strategy.

The Fourth Shock

Knowledge management is one of those terms that has been around forever and no one really seems to know what it means.

For purposes of increasing competitiveness in the Fourth Shock, the definition is quite simple: Knowledge management is the ability of an organization to intensively track what information sources, software applications and knowledge workers are adding value to the organization and which ones are not. In the period of rapid change that will be brought about by the Fourth Shock, it becomes counter-productive to try to chase every new idea. Companies must implement a system for understanding where value is being created and quickly dispense with ideas that do not create it.

In 1999, futurist Ray Kurzweil published *The Age of the Spiritual Machines* and in it he gave one of the best examples of knowledge management I have ever heard. In a discussion about how the human eye is able to process so much information so quickly, he noted that one theory on the way this works is that the eye is a kind of dual function machine. To maximize efficiency, one part of the eye acts as a still camera and takes and stores an image while a second part *only* tracks changes on the image. Because the rest of the image didn't change, there was no need to process that set of data again. The point being that the eye works so well because it knows what not to look at.

In the period of economic punctuated equilibrium that is being brought about by the Fourth Shock, companies will be deluged with ever increasing amounts of data and the applications to make that data useful. Rather than try to absorb all of it, a company would be better served by implementing a corporate-wide system for "knowing what not to look at." No one can accurately predict every possible success and failure in a period of rapid change, but by tracking utilization of information assets a company can gain insights as to what is and is not working and make adjustments accordingly.

Harkening back to the First Shock, anything going in or out of a company in the form of 0's and 1's can and should be tracked. Practically, this means data, applications and the output from the analysts and knowledge workers that use them. It constantly amazes me how little corporate executives know about how much they are spending on these assets and what impact they are having on the company's strategy.

In my discussions with senior executives about the costs associated with demand data, a concrete number is hard to come by. In one case a large company was spending $3 million per year for access to one of the major POS data aggregator's feed. *This is just for the data.* If you factor in the costs and maintenance of the computer systems to handle the data, the IT efforts to manage the data, and the analysts who use the data to find actionable insights, the total cost of a *single* data feed could approach $10 million per year.

Granted, this is the cost for a very large organization, but regardless of a company's size, there are substantial costs associated with getting demand data. Now add the fact that the number of available data feeds is growing by leaps and bounds and the average company will need to access at least a handful of them. Finally, sitting between the analysts who consume the data and the data feed itself are various software applications designed to uncover insights in the massive amounts of data and give the company a competitive advantage. Market, pricing and behavioral analytics software represent just a few of the types of applications that consume demand data and help analysts be more effective at their jobs. And like data feeds, the number and types of applications of this nature are sure to grow significantly during a period of radical technological change.

Add all of this up and the total costs for demand data at a large company can easily exceed $50 million per year. If I were the CEO of such a company I would have a few simple questions for my CIO: "Who used this stuff yesterday? How is it possible not to know this? Are we spending too much or too little? Does the software we purchased for millions of dollars add value to our business? Do our sales people actually look at the research our analysts send to them?" Every one of these is a reasonable question, but in most cases, companies simply have no idea who used what information when.

All that money goes out, all those work hours are spent, and no one really knows how much of an impact it all had on results. In the Fourth Shock, mobility and real-time POS data will create a veritable avalanche of new information streams that will need to be integrated into an organization and acted on. Sitting on top of this information will be multiple layers of software designed to give companies a competitive advantage. Leveraging both data and applications is the most important piece of all, and this ultimately means human analysts drawing insights from all of this technology and delivering packaged information to consumers, executives and the sales and marketing teams. And every piece of this information supply chain can be tracked and tied to results.[34]

To review, the four key factors that companies of every size need to start thinking about today in order to be able to seize opportunities in the Fourth Shock are:

1) The implementation of an enterprise-wide solution that allows for ever increasing numbers of demand data feeds from POS systems to be easily integrated. Feeds will be added and removed all the time and this should not impact corporate strategy or performance.

2) The implementation of a technology backbone that will allow for two-way communication with consumers in real-time. Ideally this system is integrated with the technology managing POS data

---

[34] I speak from experience on this particular topic. During the Third Shock when the Internet was being commercialized, my company SageMaker's most successful application was a knowledge management solution that tracked the usage of digital content across an organization and presented detailed, up to the minute reports to management on content utilization across the entire company.

feeds to provide the most complete view of demand data.

3) The creation of a standardized user interface so knowledge workers only have to learn a single application rather multiple applications tied to specific data feeds.

4) The implementation of an enterprise-wide knowledge management solution that is solely focused on tracking data, applications and the digital output of knowledge workers. This system should have a detailed reporting function that allows managers to know what digital assets are and are not providing value to the enterprise.

Companies that implement this technology will have the ability to capture and act on demand data trends before the rest of the supply chain and thrive in the Fourth Shock. Interacting with consumers in real-time at the point-of-purchase will create unique demand data that will become increasingly valuable over time. Combining the real-time consumer interaction data with up to the minute point-of-sale data will create unprecedented views on demand trends long before the rest of the supply chain understands the situation. This information in turn will be combined with internal and partner supply chain data to create the proactive supply chain, influencing consumer choices to squeeze more efficiencies and profits out of every transaction.

Like we saw with Google, the company that builds the largest data repository of unique consumer interactions the fastest will have a long term strategic advantage because it will have the ability to perform better trend analysis than its competitors. Therefore, first mover advantage in the Fourth Shock could prove decisive.

Once an information advantage is achieved, numerous strategies for significantly increasing profitability unfold. Whether its Enron's business model inversion strategy, Wal-Mart's embrace, empower, extend strategy, or Microsoft's strategy of consuming the most productive members of the overall supply chain, the Fourth Shock will reward those companies that most effectively manage demand data. Those companies who fall behind will find themselves at an increasingly precarious disadvantage.